S276 Geology
Science: Level 2

Book 1
Minerals, Rocks and Maps

Written by Peter Webb (Book Chair), Tom Argles and Peter Sheldon, based in part on earlier contributions by Glynda Easterbrook, Iain Gilmour, David Palmer and Mike Widdowson.

This publication forms part of the Open University course S276. Details of this and other Open University courses can be obtained from the Student Registration and Enquiry Service, The Open University, PO Box 197, Milton Keynes MK7 6BJ, United Kingdom (tel. +44 (0)845 300 60 90; email general-enquiries@open.ac.uk).

Alternatively, you may visit the Open University website at www.open.ac.uk where you can learn more about the wide range of courses and packs offered at all levels by The Open University.

To purchase a selection of Open University course materials visit www.ouw.co.uk, or contact Open University Worldwide, Walton Hall, Milton Keynes MK7 6AA, United Kingdom for a brochure (tel. +44 (0)1908 858793; fax +44 (0)1908 858787; email ouw-customer-services@open.ac.uk).

The Open University
Walton Hall, Milton Keynes
MK7 6AA

First published 2010.

Edited and designed by The Open University.

Typeset by The Open University.

Printed and bound in the United Kingdom by Halstan Printing Group, Amersham.

The paper used in this publication is procured from forests independently certified to the level of Forest Stewardship Council (FSC) principles and criteria. Chain of custody certification allows the tracing of this paper back to specific forest-management units (see www.fsc.org).

ISBN 978 1 84873553 8

2.1

The S276 Course Team

Course Team Chair
Peter Sheldon

Course Manager
Glynda Easterbrook

Main Authors
Tom Argles
Stephen Blake (Book 2 Chair)
Angela Coe
Nigel Harris
Fiona Hyden
Simon Kelley
Peter Sheldon (Book 3 Chair)
Peter Webb (Book 1 Chair)

External Course Assessor
Dr Alan Boyle
(University of Liverpool)

Other Course Team Members
Kevin Church (Consultant Reader)
Roger Courthold (Graphic Artist)
Sue Cozens (Warehouse Production Manager, Home Kit)
Sarah Davies (eLearning Advisor)
Ruth Drage (Media Project Manager)
Linda Fowler (Exam Board Chair)
Michael Francis (Media Developer, Sound and Vision)
Sarah Hack (Graphic Artist)
Chris Hough (Graphic Designer)
Richard Howes (Lead Media Assistant)
Martin Keeling (Picture Researcher)
Jane MacDougall (Consultant Reader)
Clive Mitchell (Consultant Reader)
Corinne Owen (Media Assistant)
Andrew Rix (Digital Kit video filming)
Colin Scrutton (Consultant Reader)
Bob Spicer (Reader)
Andy Sutton (Software Developer)
Andy Tindle (Digital Kit and Virtual Microscope photography)
Margaret Tindle (Kit Technician)
Pamela Wardell (Editor)

Course Secretary
Ashea Tambe

Other contributors are acknowledged in specific book, video and multimedia credits. The Course Team would also like to thank all authors and others who contributed to the previous Level 2 *Geology* course S260, from which parts of S276 are derived.

Contents

Chapter 1 Introduction

1.1 The early history and modern scope of geology

Geology is the scientific study of the Earth – its origin, history, structure and composition – and the processes involved at every scale of time and space. The prefix 'geo' comes from the Greek word for 'Earth', but many of the principles of geology derived from studying our planet can also be applied to understanding other bodies in the Solar System. You may come across, for example, the geology of Mars or lunar geology.

Geology is a relatively young science, having begun to evolve towards something like its modern form in the late 18th century through the efforts of scientists such as James Hutton (1726–1797), born in Edinburgh, and William Smith (1769–1839), born in Churchill, Oxfordshire (Figure 1.1a and b).

Hutton's revolutionary ideas may be expressed in three closely related concepts.

1 Rocks contain evidence of processes that can be seen operating today. Hutton's ideas about this were, after his time, incorporated into what became known as the **Principle of Uniformitarianism**, and condensed into the useful maxim 'the present is the key to the past'.

2 Many geological processes that can be observed, such as erosion and the deposition of sediments, cause change slowly, in small increments, but the sum of these changes can be enormous. He inferred from these slow rates that very large spans of time must be involved – orders of magnitude longer than all of human history.

3 The Earth is a dynamic planet whose surface is in a continual state of change, its materials being continuously cycled and recycled.

Hutton's first concept – uniformitarianism – was directly opposed to the religious ideas of the time, which held that geological history could be explained by a series of sudden violent events such as the Biblical Flood, a view called **catastrophism**. Hutton's second concept was also controversial, as a leading proponent of catastrophism, James Ussher (1581–1656), Archbishop of Armagh, had calculated from 'clues' in the Bible that the Earth was created in 4004 BC.

The contribution of William Smith, a surveyor and canal engineer by trade, was based on making careful notes of the fossils he collected in various layers of rock over widely separated tracts of the English countryside. Smith's observations, and his conclusions from them, led to what became known as the **Principle of Faunal Succession**: that particular groups of fossils characterise each layer, succeeding one another in a definite and recognisable order, and that the same succession of fossil groups found through older to

(a)

(b)

(c)

Figure 1.1 Three important figures in the early history of geology: (a) James Hutton; (b) William Smith; (c) Sir Charles Lyell.

younger rocks was repeated in many parts of the country. Based on this principle:

- the similar succession of fossil assemblages in different areas can be used to determine the relative ages of strata.

- rocks containing exactly the same fossils must be of the same age.

Both Hutton and Smith knew that sedimentary rocks were originally deposited in layers, known as **strata**, parallel to the Earth's surface, so that the oldest layer is at the bottom with successively younger layers resting on top. This is called the **Principle of Superposition**, and was first clearly formulated by Nicolaus Steno (1638–1686), born in Denmark.

The three separate principles of uniformitarianism, faunal succession and superposition were brought together and further developed by the Scotsman Sir Charles Lyell (1797–1875) (Figure 1.1c) in his book *Principles of Geology*, which was published in the 1830s. This book popularised the work of Hutton and Smith and led to a widespread interest in geology. These and other early geologists established the essential nature of geology as an observational science, with intensive collection and description of minerals, fossils and rocks.

The geologist may be compared to a detective or forensic scientist visiting the scene of a crime millions of years after it occurred. Just as in a crime scene investigation, careful observation and collection of data in the field are essential to working out the geological history of an area. The geologist will search for all sorts of clues in order to establish a sequence of events. Is this rock older or younger than that one? Has it been deformed, and, if so, is the disturbance due to some local event such as a landslide, or the result of regional movements of the Earth's crust over huge distances? What are the minerals in the rock, and how are they arranged? Does the rock contain fossils, mud cracks or ripple marks? And so on.

Once evidence has been gathered from rocks by making careful observations, these observations can be used to deduce the processes involved in their formation. Often, the overall objective is to reconstruct the environments in which the rocks were formed. This useful three-stage conceptual framework of making *observations*, deducing *processes* and reconstructing *environments* – i.e. observation → process → environment – is worth bearing in mind throughout the course.

Thinking in this way, it is often possible to make surprising and rewarding deductions about the geological history of an area – for example that it was once under the sea, or scorched by volcanoes, or scraped by an ice sheet. It is not unusual for a geologist, peering through a hand lens at a rock in the field, to be able to say things such as 'there was a sea here about 150 million years ago as this rock contains marine fossils from the last part of the Jurassic Period', or 'this rock must have been subjected to intense pressure during a mountain-building event', or 'this is a piece of rock from an explosive eruption'. The geologist will then assemble further evidence to confirm (or refute) his or her interpretation – in other words, carry out the fundamental scientific process of continually testing and refining a hypothesis. More-detailed work may be undertaken in the laboratory, where, for example, very thin, almost transparent, slices of rock can be studied using a microscope; the ages of rocks determined by radiometric dating of mineral grains; and the results discussed in the context of previous work on that area.

Differences of scale in space and time are a particularly interesting – and engaging – aspect of geology. Arguably, no other science routinely involves changes of scale so often. The processes of geology range from the split-second decay of individual radioactive atoms in a tiny crystal to the slow movement of the Earth's vast tectonic plates over millions of years. Such seemingly disparate processes and scales are intimately connected. The tectonic plates are made of rocks, rocks are made of minerals, minerals are made of atoms, and atoms are made of subatomic particles (Figure 1.2). Some atoms are unstable, breaking down to give different chemical elements, and releasing radiation. The heat from this radioactive decay, along with accretionary heat from the early formation of the Earth, escapes upwards to the surface and drives the movements of the tectonic plates. These movements produce many large-scale features of the Earth's surface, from mountain ranges to deep ocean trenches, and cause dramatic, often life-threatening, events such as volcanic eruptions, earthquakes and tsunamis. The connectedness across these scales, and the relevance to human lives, is clear.

Before going any further, let's consider a few definitions, some of which will be elaborated later. A **rock** is a solid, naturally occurring assemblage of mineral grains. The grains may all be of the same mineral, but more often a rock consists of an assemblage of different minerals. A **mineral** is a naturally formed, solid substance that has a regular arrangement of atoms which limits its chemical composition and gives it a characteristic crystal shape. Rocks may be divided into three groups according to how they were formed.

- **Igneous rocks** are formed by the cooling and solidification, usually crystallisation, of molten rock (**magma**), either inside the Earth or on its surface. Magma flowing at the surface is called **lava**, as is the rock formed when it solidifies. Most igneous rocks are characterised by an interlocking crystalline texture, though some are glassy and others have a fragmental texture.

- **Sedimentary rocks** are formed by the accumulation of sediment that is deposited on the Earth's surface by water, air or ice. Most sediments have a fragmental texture, consisting of fragments of pre-existing rocks and mineral grains, or the hard parts of organisms. Some sediments are composed of minerals precipitated during the evaporation of salty water. During burial, sediments are compacted and cemented together to form sedimentary rocks.

- **Metamorphic rocks** form when rocks of any original type (igneous, sedimentary or metamorphic) are changed by heat and/or pressure. They have an interlocking crystalline texture and often display mineral alignment or banding. They contain new crystals, often of quite different minerals from the original ones. Under very high temperatures, metamorphic rocks can begin to melt and so produce new magmas.

Figure 1.2 Diagram to show the typically wide range of spatial scales over which geology continually operates. Arranged around the Earth seen from space are, clockwise from the top: a silicon atom (with electrons orbiting around a nucleus with protons and neutrons); the internal structure of quartz (the small black spheres represent silicon atoms; larger, light-coloured spheres represent oxygen atoms); a quartz crystal (4 cm long); an exposure of gneiss in the Himalaya; folded rocks in the northern Himalaya; a mountain in the Himalaya (Ama Dablam); the Himalaya seen from space. A meteorite approaching the Earth represents extraterrestrial influences. See text for further discussion of scales in space and time.

Over millions of years, one type of rock can turn into another, and then another, in cycles that have been occurring for billions of years. This means that the component atoms of a piece of the Earth's crust can have an extraordinarily rich individual history. Imagine picking up a grain of sand from a beach and being able to trace where any one of its atoms of silicon had been during the last billion years. A silicon atom may once have been part of a quartz crystal that formed deep down in a granite intrusion. At other times it may have been in a feldspar crystal at the top of a mountain, dissolved in the ocean, incorporated into the body of a now-extinct organism, and located in a metamorphic rock buried way below the Earth's surface – the possibilities are almost endless. Another silicon atom might have a quite different story to tell – like two coins in your pocket that have passed through different hands in diverse places to get to where they are now.

In the early days of geology, the idea that 'the present is the key to the past' was an important concept, and it still is. Today, however, there is also a new, and more urgent, perspective. With concerns about global warming and other effects of climate change, understanding the past is seen as the key to the future. The Earth is a web of complex, interconnected and open systems linking the planet's interior with its atmosphere, oceans and biosphere. Understanding how these interact over time is an approach known as Earth System Science. Such an interdisciplinary approach, however, depends on a good grounding in geology – an understanding of the rocks, minerals, fossils and geological structures that provide hard evidence about the Earth's processes and its history. Geology itself uses many of the principles of physics, chemistry and biology, and to many people the interdisciplinary nature of geology is part of its appeal.

The Earth is not an isolated system. We sometimes need to look far beyond the Earth to understand events in its history: extraterrestrial factors need to be considered. For example, there is compelling evidence that 65 million years ago, at the end of the Cretaceous Period, a large meteorite struck what is now the coast of Mexico – an event that almost certainly contributed to some of the many species extinctions at that time. The scope of geology is wide indeed.

In this first book of the course, you will briefly consider the geological timescale. Then follows an introduction to geological maps, including the geological map of the UK, which is an area with an exceptionally wide range of rock types and rock ages for its size. Next, in a change of scale typical of geology, you will look at various properties of minerals and learn how different minerals can be identified, especially when viewed as thin slices under a petrological microscope using polarised light. After studying the main rock-forming minerals, you will move on to look at the major features of igneous, sedimentary and metamorphic rocks. Then, tying these various aspects together, the relationship between landscapes and their underlying geology is considered, and the book finishes by revealing how geological history can be read from geological maps.

1.2 The geological timescale

Evidence of coral reefs apparently now stranded in the hills of northern England (Figure 1.3), along with numerous other fossils, convinced pioneering geologists of the 19th century that a long history was written in the rocks. But how long was that history? How old was the Earth?

James Hutton was able to determine the *order* in which rocks formed – their relative ages – by examining the physical relationships among rocks. Later geologists applied the principle of faunal succession to compare and correlate

(a)   (b)

Figure 1.3   (a) A Carboniferous coral reef exposed on a hillside in northern England. Reproduced with the permission of the British Geological Survey © NERC. All rights Reserved. (b) A Carboniferous coral from northern England.

rock strata across the world, constructing a *relative* geological timescale that indicated the sequence in which events occurred. Since each fossil species existed for an interval of time and then became extinct, the first and last occurrences of each fossil bracket a particular interval of geological time. This painstaking compilation, chiefly carried out in the 19th century, resulted in one of the great achievements of science: the geological timescale. In Figure 1.4, this scale is divided into **Eons**, **Eras** and **Periods**, with the time divisions arranged in chronological order from the oldest at the bottom to the youngest at the top. The result is a **stratigraphic column**, arranged just as sedimentary rocks of these ages would be stacked now if they had been left undisturbed since they were laid down.

Notice that Figure 1.4 also shows ages as numbers. These absolute ages, given in millions of years (Ma), were added in the 20th century. In the 19th century, estimates of the spans of time represented by different thicknesses of rocks implied that the Earth was at least several hundred million years old. However, in 1865 the physicist Lord Kelvin determined the age of the Earth to be between 20 and 40 Ma: the time needed for an originally molten Earth to cool. Later, studies of the rates of decay of radioactive isotopes led to radiometric dating of rocks, and these dates showed Kelvin's estimate for the age of the Earth to be much too small. This discrepancy is mainly because heat is continuously being produced within the Earth by radioactive decay, thus slowing the rate at which the planet cools. Kelvin's work was done about 30 years before radioactivity was discovered, so his calculations did not include this extra heat source. From time to time, new results cause minor revisions of key dates in the geological record (which explains why you may find dates elsewhere that differ from those used in this course), but the essence of the timescale in Figure 1.4 is not generally in doubt.

The true span of geological time revealed by the absolute dates surprised geologists. Analysis of certain meteorites (Figure 1.5), believed to be the oldest surviving material in the Solar System, indicate that the Earth was formed about 4600 Ma ago. Further work has revealed that much of the fossil record on which the relative timescale is based spans only the past 540 Ma,

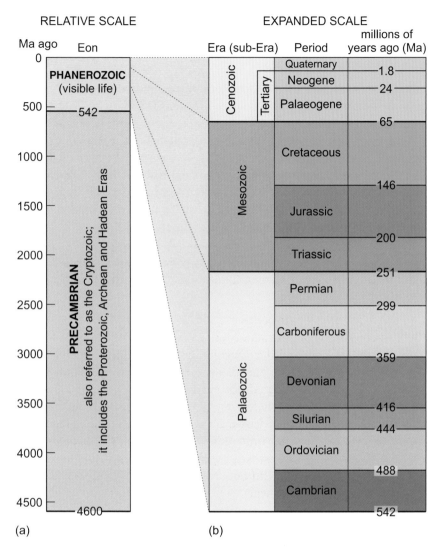

Figure 1.4 Stratigraphic column for the whole of geological time: (a) to true scale; (b) expanded scale since the onset of the Cambrian. The scale is divided into Eons, Eras and Periods. In (a), note the length of the Precambrian, which lasted for about 90% of all geological time.

with older fossils being both rare and often poorly preserved. The expanse of time represented by an age of 4600 Ma is difficult to grasp within human experience and is perhaps best treated by analogy.

If the entire 4600 Ma of geological time is compressed into a single calendar year, then the oldest rocks known on Earth, the 4030 million-year-old Acasta Gneiss in Canada, date from Valentine's Day (14 February). Although soft-bodied marine life probably first appeared during early March, no life appeared on land until late November. The widespread forests and swamps that formed the coal deposits of much of Europe flourished for about four days in early December. The dinosaurs were in their heyday in mid-December but disappeared around the time a large meteorite hit the Earth at lunchtime on 26 December. Human-like primates appeared in the late evening of 31 December and the last ice age ended around 1 minute and 15 seconds

Figure 1.5 A 4600 million-year-old meteorite, with flecks of metallic iron on the cut face. The smooth outer surface was formed by melting as it plummeted through the Earth's atmosphere. The meteorite is 7 cm across.

before midnight on that day. Columbus arrived in America some three seconds before midnight and James Hutton conceived the Principle of Uniformitarianism slightly more than one second before the end of the year.

One of geology's most significant contributions to modern science is the recognition of this immense span of geological time. Over the past 500 Ma (less than one-ninth of the Earth's history), plate tectonic movement has resulted in the progressive northerly drift of the British Isles region from some 65° south of the Equator to around 55° north. As a result, the rocks of the British Isles reflect a sometimes turbulent geological history: from ancient mountain ranges and the remains of long-extinct volcanoes formed during plate collisions, to limestone laid down in tropical coral seas, to sandstones formed from the remnants of desert sand dunes (Figure 1.6).

(a)

(b)

(c)

(d)

Figure 1.6 From coral seas to deserts: views of NE England, looking west towards the Lake District, reconstructed for four different geological times from the Early Carboniferous to the Late Permian. During its progressive northward drift, this part of Britain developed a wide range of environments in which many different rocks were formed and later preserved. Hard Ordovician volcanic rocks lie at the heart of the Lake District, forming much of the high ground. During the Early Carboniferous (a), the region lay close to the Equator and the lowlands to the east were submerged by a shallow sea in which corals and other marine organisms flourished. As this sea receded, it was replaced in turn by coal swamps of the Late Carboniferous (b) and then deserts in the Early Permian (c) as the British Isles region moved north from the Equator and approached the present latitude of the Sahara. By the Late Permian (d), a shallow sea had encroached once more.

Activity 1.1 Time for geology

Read the notes on Activity 1.1 in *Workbook 1* and then watch the video *Geological time*, which explores a number of concepts concerning time in geology.

Instructions and notes on the activities are in a separate loose-leaf booklet, *Workbook 1*. You will need to refer to that booklet before starting each activity. Try to do each activity as you come to it in the text – however, we understand that this may not always be convenient and that you may have to do some later than is ideal. It may be worthwhile, especially if you are studying away from home, to consult the Workbook to find out in advance what you will need for the activities coming up.

1.3 Geological maps

The complex geological history of an area can be succinctly summarised in a geological map, which shows both the ages of different rock types, and the spatial relationships between them, along with a key (also known as a legend, explanation or index) explaining the symbols and colours used on the map.

1.3.1 A simple geological map of Britain and Ireland

Geological maps of large areas, like the small map of Britain and Ireland shown in Figure 1.7, simplify data compiled from many maps that cover much smaller areas in greater detail. You will see from the key to Figure 1.7 that the sedimentary rocks are divided into four main groups – **Cenozoic**, **Mesozoic**, **Palaeozoic** and **Upper Proterozoic** – which correspond to particular spans of time in the stratigraphic column of Figure 1.4. The first three groups are called Eras of geological time and together constitute the **Phanerozoic** Eon. Time before the Phanerozoic is divided into three other Eras (not shown on Figure 1.4), the **Proterozoic**, the **Archean** and the **Hadean**, which together constitute the **Precambrian** Eon. The term Upper Proterozoic on the map refers to the most recent part of the Proterozoic Era. The Eras of the Phanerozoic are themselves divided into Periods (e.g. Cambrian, Permian; see Figure 1.4). For the sedimentary rocks, each colour represents rocks formed during a particular Period.

The stratigraphic column is one of the most important features of the key on any geological map. Sedimentary units are always arranged in **stratigraphical order**, from the oldest at the bottom to the youngest at the top. Igneous and metamorphic rocks have their own columns, which commonly depart from this principle. Hence, on Figure 1.7, metamorphic rocks are divided into two main groups according to when they were metamorphosed, while igneous rocks are not classified by age, but are divided into just two categories: **intrusive rocks** and **extrusive rocks** (Sections 6.3 and 6.4) – not because their ages are unknown, but merely to simplify the map.

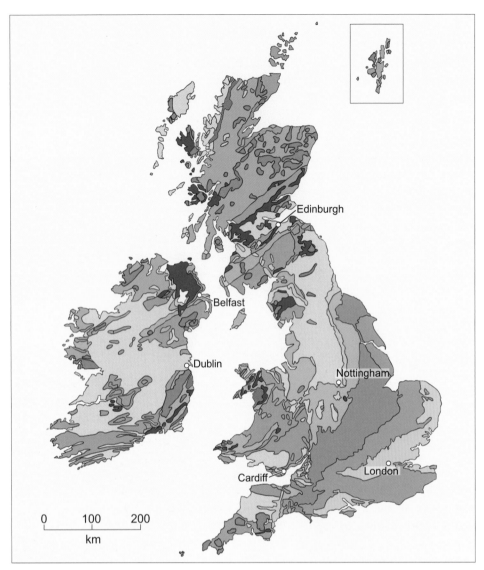

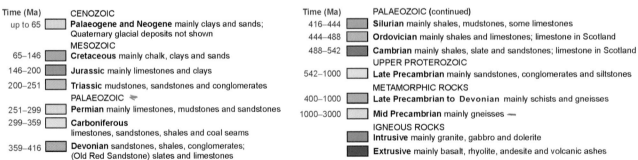

Time (Ma)	CENOZOIC
up to 65	**Palaeogene and Neogene** mainly clays and sands; Quaternary glacial deposits not shown
	MESOZOIC
65–146	**Cretaceous** mainly chalk, clays and sands
146–200	**Jurassic** mainly limestones and clays
200–251	**Triassic** mudstones, sandstones and conglomerates
	PALAEOZOIC
251–299	**Permian** mainly limestones, mudstones and sandstones
299–359	**Carboniferous** limestones, sandstones, shales and coal seams
359–416	**Devonian** sandstones, shales, conglomerates; (Old Red Sandstone) slates and limestones

Time (Ma)	PALAEOZOIC (continued)
416–444	**Silurian** mainly shales, mudstones, some limestones
444–488	**Ordovician** mainly shales and limestones; limestone in Scotland
488–542	**Cambrian** mainly shales, slate and sandstones; limestone in Scotland
	UPPER PROTEROZOIC
542–1000	**Late Precambrian** mainly sandstones, conglomerates and siltstones
	METAMORPHIC ROCKS
400–1000	**Late Precambrian to Devonian** mainly schists and gneisses
1000–3000	**Mid Precambrian** mainly gneisses
	IGNEOUS ROCKS
	Intrusive mainly granite, gabbro and dolerite
	Extrusive mainly basalt, rhyolite, andesite and volcanic ashes

Figure 1.7   Geological map of Britain and Ireland.

You should now answer the following questions, which are intended to consolidate your grasp of the relationship between the stratigraphic column of a geological map and the map itself.

Question 1.1

Using the key in conjunction with the map in Figure 1.7 (and, perhaps, an atlas to identify places), where are the oldest and youngest rocks found?

Question 1.2

Imagine that you are travelling in a perfectly straight line from London to Edinburgh. Write down in sequence the ages of the rocks (i.e. the Periods) you would pass over on this journey. (Ignore the red and purple patches of igneous rocks in the northern part of the journey.)

From your answers to Questions 1.1 and 1.2, you should now know that not only are the oldest rocks in the northwest of Britain and the youngest in the southeast but also, for much of the intervening distance, the rocks become progressively older from London northwards. The progression is not usually as regular as along this line from London to Edinburgh, but the trend in Britain is generally towards older rocks to the north and west.

Question 1.3

With reference to Figure 1.7 (and, perhaps, an atlas):

(a) Where are the main areas of metamorphic rocks?
(b) Where are the areas with intrusive and extrusive (volcanic) igneous rocks? Are they associated mainly with metamorphic rocks or with sedimentary rocks?

Importantly, although every Period is represented on the simplified geological map of Britain and Ireland by a single colour, each may include a variety of rock types. This simplification is necessary to be able to show the geology of Britain and Ireland on such a small map. If you open one of your BGS Bedrock Geology UK Map sheets (either UK South or UK North), you will notice that they show a great deal more detail within Periods, often with shades of a particular colour for each type of rock or group of closely related rocks. On larger-scale maps of smaller areas, it is possible to show more geological detail, even down to an individual layer (usually called a **bed**) of rock. Thus, a key on such a map relates not only to particular time divisions but also to particular beds of rock.

Throughout the rest of the course, we will refer to this map using the shorter name Bedrock UK Map, adding (S) or (N) when we are referring to just the South or North sheet, respectively.

You should now familiarise yourself with the names of the Eons, Eras and Periods from Figure 1.4 and/or Figure 1.7, though you do not need to remember any of the numerical dates.

Activity 1.2   Geology of Britain: an outline

This activity concerns a major geological division of Britain and how this relates to large-scale topography. You will need to refer to Figure 1.7 in this book as you do this activity.

1.3.2 A brief history of geological and topographic mapping

The first geological maps, published in 1797, used data from **geological cross-sections** produced for mines throughout the 18th century (e.g. Figure 1.8). The map makers (cartographers) depicted areas of different rock types in contrasting ways: William Maton (1774–1835) used line shading, while William Smith employed different colours.

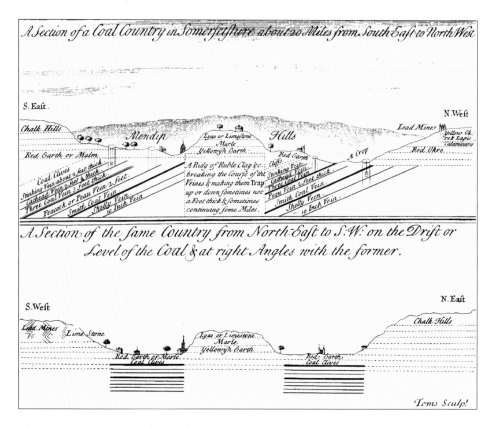

Figure 1.8 Cross-sections of the Somerset coalfield, published in 1725.

Section 1.1 described how Smith realised that particular groups of fossils characterised each rock layer (**stratum**) of a particular age, and thus established the idea of a stratigraphic column in England. He coloured each stratum according to its relative age, tracing the strata from Yorkshire down to Somerset. His work culminated in a geological map of England, Wales and southern Scotland, published in 1815 on 15 sheets, an extract of which is shown in Figure 1.9. He later produced maps of 21 counties on a larger scale.

Smith drew the geology on an accurate **topographic map**, a novelty at that time in Britain, and essential for precise location of geological boundaries. Today, the **Ordnance Survey** (OS) and the **British Geological Survey** (BGS) publish topographical and geological maps, respectively, in Britain, using standardised map scales and the **National Grid** system for locating features in Britain (see Box 1.1 and Figure 1.10). You will encounter examples of such maps, and those from other countries, throughout the course.

Figure 1.9   An extract from William Smith's geological map published in 1815, drawn on a base map supplied by the publisher J. Cary. Smith faded the colour away from the base of each stratum, emphasising the three-dimensional nature of the beds.

One problem for early map makers was portraying a three-dimensional landscape on a flat piece of paper; hills and slopes were shown diagrammatically (Figure 1.11a) or with hachured shading (Figure 1.11b). Contour lines representing variations in surface elevation (**relief**) were first drawn by Charles Hutton in 1774–76, for the mountain Schiehallion (Figure 1.11c) in Scotland. Each contour line represents the intersection between the land surface and an imaginary horizontal plane at a specific height above mean sea level; this reference plane is known as **ordnance datum** (OD). **Contours** were in regular use by 1850 by the Board of Ordnance, founded in 1791 to survey Britain for the British Army. From as early as 1835, geologists worked alongside surveyors for the Board of Ordnance.

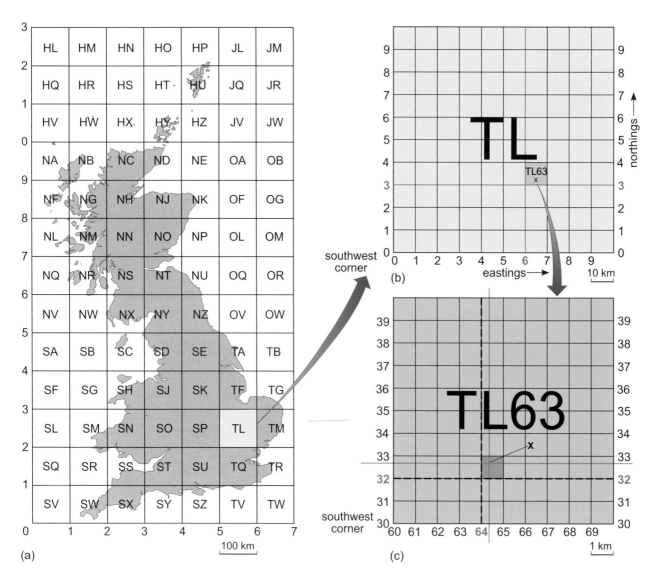

Figure 1.10 (a) The United Kingdom National Grid. Each square is 100 × 100 km and is represented by either a two-letter code or the two numbers of the grid lines that intersect at the square's southwest corner. (b) 100 km grid squares can be further subdivided into a 10 km-spaced grid. Using these 10 km grid lines, it is possible to specify any 10 km grid square by quoting first the easting and then the northing lines that intersect at the southwest corner of the 10 km square (bold lines). (c) The 10 km grid is divided into a 1 km grid on 1 : 50 000 and larger-scale maps. Using the eastings and northings and by estimating the distance between the 1 km grid lines, it is possible to specify any point in the UK to within 100 metres.

Box 1.1   The National Grid

The National Grid is in effect a grid overlain on a map of Britain (Figure 1.10a). This grid is divided into 100 km squares, each identified by two letters; for example, the 100 km grid square that encompasses the Isle of Wight on the south coast of England is SZ, while the 100 km grid square that encompasses Edinburgh is NT. Alternatively, the same grid squares can each be identified by a pair of numbers in brackets after the letters (i.e. SZ (40) and NT (36) for these two examples). Any point in the UK can be located on a map using its **grid reference**.

■ How many kilometres are represented by the distance between the bottom of the grid in Figure 1.10a and the bottom of the southernmost N grid squares (NV, NW, NX, etc.)?

□ This distance is 500 km.

Lines running north–south on the grid are referred to as **eastings**, while the lines that run east–west are called **northings**. If this seems confusing, consider the following question.

■ In Figure 1.10a, if you move from grid square SZ on the south coast to SU, SP, SK and so on, you cross a series of northing lines, like the rungs of a ladder. In which direction are you moving?

□ You are moving *north*. This is the origin of the term northing.

The term 'easting' derives in a similar way, and these names illustrate an important principle for grid references: grid numbers increase *eastwards* and *northwards*. The grid line at the bottom of the N grid squares NV, NW, NX and so on, is referred to as the 500 km northing because it is 500 km north of the bottom of the grid.

The 100 km grid squares are further divided into smaller squares by grid lines at a 10 km spacing, each numbered 0 to 9 from the southwest corner in an easterly (left to right) and northerly (upwards) direction. For example, Figure 1.10b shows the further division of the 100 km grid square TL (52). Using this system, you can identify any 10 km grid square by giving first the two-letter code (with or without the two-number code in brackets) for the 100 km grid square followed by the easting and then the northing on the 10 km grid. So for example, in Figure 1.10b you can identify the highlighted 10 km grid square as TL63 (or, alternatively, TL (52) 63).

On 1 : 50 000 OS map sheets, the 100 km grid square(s) covered by the sheet are printed just inside the corners of the map, and are shown on a diagram in the margin. At this or larger scales, the grid is further divided into 1 km intervals as shown in Figure 1.10c. As with the 10 km grid, you begin in the southwest corner and quote first the eastings and then the northings. In Figure 1.10c, the point at the intersection of the two dashed lines identifies the green 1 km grid square TL (52) 6432 by its southwest corner.

By estimating the distance between the 1 km grid lines, you can specify a position to within 100 metres. For example, the 100 metre grid reference for the point X shown in Figure 1.10c at the intersection of the two thin blue lines is TL (52) 643327. If the map you are working with lies entirely within a 100 km grid square, the TL (52) prefix can be omitted.

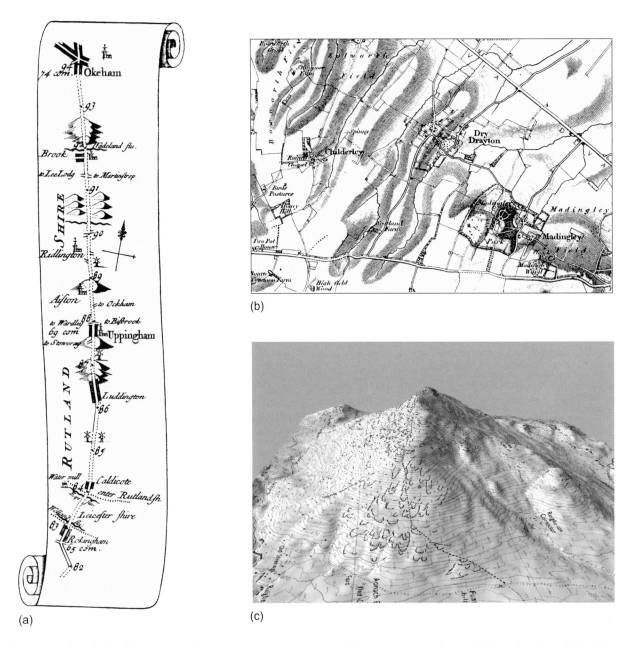

(a)

(b)

(c)

Figure 1.11 Relief on early and modern maps. (a) Detail from a map of the road from London to Oakham (spelt 'Okeham' on the map) in Rutland, England, drawn by John Sennex (1719). Scale approximately 0.5 inch to 1 mile. (b) Detail from the Cambridge sheet of the first Ordnance Survey One-Inch Survey of England and Wales (1836). Scale 1 inch to 1 mile. (c) Extract from a modern Ordnance Survey 1 : 50 000 scale map of Schiehallion, draped onto a digital elevation model, viewed from the east. This mountain in Scotland is where contour lines were first devised, by Hutton. Hutton invented contour lines to simplify the calculation of the volume of Schiehallion as part of an experiment to determine the gravitational constant.

1.3.3   Modern geological maps and the digital age

Colour is an essential ingredient in modern geological maps, whether they are printed on paper or viewed on a computer screen. So, what exactly do the colours represent? On many geological maps, the coloured areas are interpretations of where different types of solid rock, the **bedrock**, would occur if everything obscuring them – vegetation, glaciers, buildings, roads, industrial debris and soil – was removed. In addition, there may be other, unconsolidated geological materials known collectively as **superficial deposits** or drift, which were deposited during the Quaternary. Such materials include glacial clay, river gravels, alluvium, peat, and beach sands. Figure 1.12a is an extract from a 1 : 50 000 map showing *only* these superficial deposits, some of which can be valuable resources. (Box 1.2 includes a brief summary of the concept of map scales, with some examples.)

Figure 1.12b shows the solid or bedrock geology for the same area as Figure 1.12a. The colours in this case represent what geologists call the **outcrop**, the areas where particular rocks are presumed to lie beneath any superficial deposits. It indicates, for instance, that sandstone forms the bedrock at A (Llaniler), but moving SSE to B (Rhos-y-garth) the bedrock changes to mudstone.

How is such a geological map made? In the field, the geologist examines rock where it is actually visible at the surface, for instance in a crag, cliff, quarry, or beach platform; rock exposed like this is known as an **exposure**. Characteristics such as rock composition, internal structure and fossil content are recorded, enabling different groups of rock to be distinguished and shown separately on the base map. Of course, although the whole of a map area is shown coloured according to the rocks present, this does not imply that at any point rocks of that particular type are actually visible at the surface, or that a geologist has visited every exposure to record the rock type.

In areas that lack surface exposures, the nature of the bedrock must be deduced from data such as the type of soil, surface landforms, and information from boreholes, by applying basic geological principles to produce a plausible configuration. This introduces an important consideration: even the process of actually making a map is interpretative, so no map should necessarily be regarded as being absolutely correct. Nevertheless, maps such as the Bedrock UK Map North and South sheets are unlikely to undergo radical revision tomorrow as a result of a new geological exposure because these maps show only a broad picture of the geology. However, a more detailed map, such as the Cheddar Sheet that you will use later, could be revised if new exposures were revealed – during the construction of a new road, for example.

The colours or shades on the map are separated from each other by sharp boundaries (Figure 1.12b). These geological boundaries are lines showing where surfaces separating different kinds of rocks in the ground intersect the topographic surface and they allow the areal extent, size and shape of the various bodies of rock to be determined. The geologist makes a map by recognising in the field where one kind of rock ends and another begins, indicating that change by a line on the map. Nevertheless, there are always parts of the map where uncertainty exists about the nature of the bedrock (for instance under glaciers in the Alps), and it is important to realise that a good deal of interpretation is used in the map-making process and that not all maps are based on equal amounts of information.

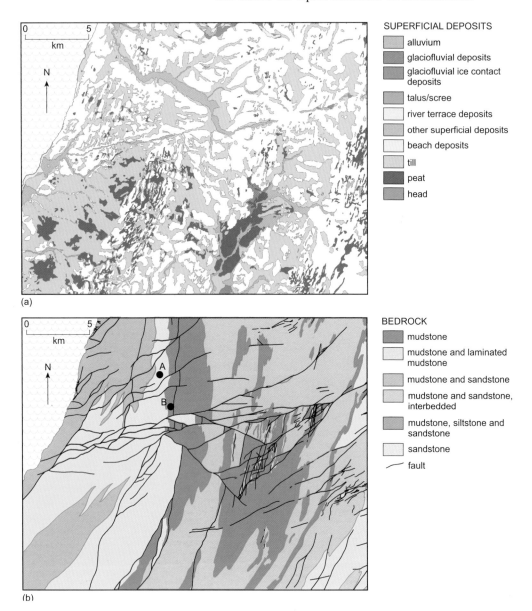

SUPERFICIAL DEPOSITS

- alluvium
- glaciofluvial deposits
- glaciofluvial ice contact deposits
- talus/scree
- river terrace deposits
- other superficial deposits
- beach deposits
- till
- peat
- head

(a)

BEDROCK

- mudstone
- mudstone and laminated mudstone
- mudstone and sandstone
- mudstone and sandstone, interbedded
- mudstone, siltstone and sandstone
- sandstone
- fault

(b)

Figure 1.12 (a) Extract from the 1 : 50 000 digital geological map of Llaniler, west Wales, showing only superficial deposits. (b) Extract from the digital geological map of the same area as part (a), showing the solid (bedrock) geology. Some terms may be unfamiliar, but the importance of this figure lies in the contrasting map patterns in (a) and (b). Both maps are derived from BGS data.

Box 1.2 Scale in geological maps

Basic field mapping is generally carried out on a relatively large scale, such as 1 : 10 000. This means that 1 cm on the map represents 10 000 cm (100 m) on the ground, so these maps can show considerable detail. Before about 1980, similar maps in Britain were produced at a scale of 1 : 10 560 (6 inches to 1 mile). Most of the maps in this course are at a smaller scale than this, so that features on the map are very small relative to their actual size in the field. However, smaller-scale maps:

- can show greater areas on the same size sheet
- tend to simplify the detail mapped at larger scales, to maintain clarity.

Table 1.1 summarises some aspects of geological maps at different scales.

Geological maps published by the BGS are based on Ordnance Survey topographic maps. Both OS and BGS maps are referred to as sheets because there is a lot of other information printed on the sheet around the edges of the actual map. The most common scale which the British Geological Survey uses is 1 : 50 000 for published maps, which have largely replaced the original 1 inch to 1 mile (1 : 63 360) maps.

Maps at a larger scale of 1 : 25 000 exist for some areas in Britain, showing greater detail (e.g. field boundaries), and making it easy to locate particular features, while still covering a reasonably large area. With the development of different methods for mapping offshore, the BGS have also published maps at the scale of 1 : 250 000 that not only cover a much larger area but also include sea-floor geology as well as that on land.

Table 1.1 Comparison of geological maps at different scales.

Scale	Map distances	Uluru* length	Example of map at this scale	Comments
1 : 10 000	1 cm = 100 m	31.0 cm	ST76SW Bath (BGS)	Field mapping of a local area
1 : 10 560	6 inches = 1 mile	29.4 cm	NZ35NE Sunderland (BGS)	Pre-1980 UK detailed maps
1 : 25 000	1 cm = 250 m	12.4 cm	Cheddar (BGS)	Areas of special interest (UK)
1 : 50 000	1 cm = 500 m	6.2 cm	Snowdon (BGS)	20 × 30 km sheets in UK
1 : 63 360	1 inch = 1 mile	4.9 cm	Lizard Head (1839) (BGS)	Based on pre-metric grid
1 : 250 000	1 cm = 2.5 km	1.24 cm	Lake District (BGS); Mount Bruce (Geoscience Australia)	Regional scale; includes offshore geology in UK
1 : 625 000	1 cm = 6.25 km	0.5 cm	Bedrock UK Map (BGS)	2 sheets (N and S) covering the whole of Britain
1 : 1 000 000	1 cm = 10 km	0.31 cm	Montana (USGS)	State maps in United States
1 : 25 000 000	1 cm = 250 km	0.01 mm	World (CGMW/UNESCO)	Maps at planet scale

Handwritten annotations in left margin: "Detail ↓ Large" near top of table; "Small scale" near bottom of table.

* A sandstone hill in central Australia (see Question 1.4 and Figure 1.13).

Figure 1.13 Aerial photograph of Uluru (formerly known as Ayers Rock), central Australia.

Question 1.4

Using the metric data given in Table 1.1 (in Box 1.2), calculate the actual length (in kilometres) of Uluru, an isolated sandstone hill in central Australia (Figure 1.13). Express your answer to 2 significant figures.

1.3.4 Digital geological maps and geographic information systems

Advances in computing have radically changed both the production of geological maps and how they are used. Powerful computer systems can now collect, assemble, store, manipulate, analyse and display all kinds of geographical data in a spatial context. The combination of computer hardware, software and data is known as a **Geographic Information System** (GIS), and such systems are becoming a part of daily life for many people who use them, for example, to plan car journeys or check the location of a hotel. But a GIS also affects us in more subtle ways: it is used in every conceivable situation from marketing to military applications, and even in the exploration of other planets.

One powerful aspect of a GIS is its ability to integrate different kinds of data that are referenced to the same location (Figure 1.14), so it plays an important role in connecting geology to modern society, especially where development and environmental issues are concerned. Take, for example, a specific disused quarry that has been proposed as a landfill site. A GIS allows environmental geologists to retrieve a range of information on that site and its surroundings, either from files stored on the computer or on a remote server accessed via the internet, for example:

- aerial photographs and satellite images can be overlain on the geological map as a visual guide, and the distribution of different soils or vegetation cover can be included in the analysis

- leachate from the site may pose a pollution threat if porous rocks occur in the vicinity of the quarry. The distribution of such rocks can be plotted using the GIS, and hydrological data can be used to predict the path that any pollution would take, and to identify which areas would be most affected

- the GIS could answer all sorts of related questions that might arise, such as how close are local villages, rivers and reservoirs? What is the prevailing wind direction? How many people live within 5 km of the site?

This kind of analytical function enables conclusions to be drawn about the site's *environmental sensitivity*. A GIS can also recognise and analyse the spatial relationships between mapped phenomena. Conditions of *adjacency* (what is next to what), *containment* (what is enclosed by what), and *proximity* (how close something is to something else) can all be determined, as can changes of these attributes over time.

A critical feature of a GIS is its ability to produce on-screen or printed graphics that convey the results of analyses clearly; for example to generate a customised map that ranks proposed landfill sites according to their environmental impact.

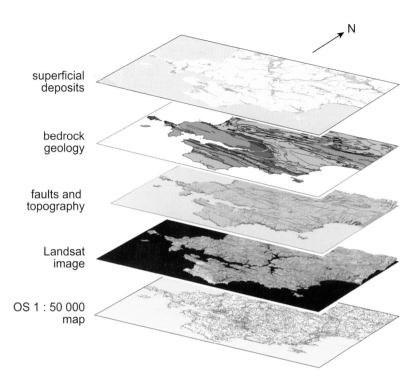

N

superficial
deposits

bedrock
geology

faults and
topography

Landsat
image

OS 1 : 50 000
map

Figure 1.14 An illustration of several datasets for part of southwest Wales stored in a GIS and displayed as stacked layers with their geographic locations preserved. Some of the layers are draped over a 3D topographic model of the area. Details not resolved in this figure could be viewed at much larger scales in the digital file on a computer.

Hence, a digital geological map may contain far more information than just the solid or superficial geology. Topography, borehole records, seismic, gravity or magnetic data, the location of resources or hazards, and details of fossil or chemical features can also be included. The skill of the geologist is then to select the most relevant data and display it clearly in the most appropriate form for the audience.

1.4   The Bedrock UK Map

The wonderfully varied geology of the whole of Britain and Northern Ireland is covered in two BGS map sheets, UK North and UK South, at a scale of 1 : 625 000 (1 inch to roughly 10 miles). Note that there is an 80 km overlap between the two sheets in northern England. The maps show major roads, railways and rivers as well as towns, but no contours. These maps are a constant source of information and interest on journeys around the UK. The red grid overprinted on the maps shows the boundaries of the larger scale One-Inch (1 : 63 360) and 1 : 50 000 geological sheets. The British National Grid is overprinted in grey to allow easy reference to any locality by a series of digits (its National Grid reference), which can be found on OS maps at any scale. A diagram in the margin of the two Bedrock UK Map sheets (N and S) shows the letters and alternative numbers (e.g. TL (52)) for the 100 km grid squares covered by each sheet. In addition, each 10 km grid line on the main maps is labelled with two numbers. The *larger* number refers to 10 km divisions *within* the 100 km grid square (i.e. the 6 and 3 in TL (52) shown on Figure 1.10b), while the *smaller* number relates to the 100 km grid square (i.e. the 5 and 2 in TL (52) shown on Figure 1.10a). The small numbers make finding grid-referenced features on the two sheets easier than trying to match the two letters on the marginal diagram to the main map, because the letters are not marked on the main map at all. You should now check this out for yourself on your copy of the map.

■   What is the name of the city centred on grid reference SE (44) 6152?

☐   York. Grid square SE (44) covers an area of northern England west of the Humber estuary. The 10 km grid square SE (44) 65 lies northwest of the Humber Estuary, near the city of York. The centre of York lies near the lower-left corner of this 10 km square, about 1 km east of the easting line marked ^{4}6, and about 2 km north of the northing line marked ^{4}5.

You will notice that the maps are entitled 'Bedrock Geology': they show the different **rock units** as if all superficial deposits have been removed from above the beds of solid rock. A note below the main title indicates that the North and South sheets each overlap the 500 km Northing National Grid line by 40 km.

Each sheet has an index showing different rock groups and other features, such as geological boundaries and faults. The sheets provide full explanations of the rather complicated colour schemes used to depict different rock units, but a few main points can be emphasised here. Sedimentary and metamorphic rocks are arranged in stratigraphic order (see Figure 1.7) in an almost continuous column of coloured boxes. To the left of the column are different time divisions (Eras, Periods, and **Epochs** or **Ages**), with some important radiometric dates in red (on the extreme left). Each of the main Periods is assigned a letter (e.g. J for Jurassic) that forms part of the label for each rock unit in the column, with numbers denoting their position within the Period.

Information on **lithology** – general characteristics of rocks such as colour, texture and mineral composition – is provided to the right of the column, along with names of some of the common rock units, so this is a **lithostratigraphic** column. However, the column is *not* to scale in terms of time or strata thickness. Extra columns to the right show strata in certain regions where their lithology differs markedly from those in the main column, perhaps because they were laid down under very different conditions. These rock units are correlated with those in the main column because they are of the same proven age, despite having a different lithology. Conversely, rocks of similar lithology cannot be correlated from one area to another unless it can be proved that they are of equivalent age. The North sheet shows fewer sedimentary units and more metamorphic units than the South sheet, because of the different histories of the two regions; much of the Scottish Highlands is underlain by metamorphic rocks that are considerably older than any rocks exposed in southern Britain.

The index of igneous rocks is arranged similarly by age, with separate boxes that reflect the more restricted periods in which they formed. They are divided into intrusive and extrusive (volcanic) rocks, with colour schemes based on their compositions that are simpler than the colour schemes for the sedimentary/metamorphic rocks. An important difference between the two sheets is that extrusive igneous rocks of the Palaeogene Period are present in western Scotland, particularly on the islands of Skye (grid square NG (18)) and Mull (NM (17)).

The last items in the index are geological boundaries, major **faults** and thrusts (a type of fault). Faults are more or less planar fractures along which movement of one side has occurred relative to the other side. You will examine some prominent UK faults in more detail in Chapter 11. On the North sheet, there is even a separate box beneath the sedimentary and metamorphic rock index for rocks formed in fault zones. Another prominent feature of this sheet is the more or less regular pattern of dark-green lines of basaltic rock that run northwest–southeast across much of western Scotland. These igneous rocks have been intruded into the crust along steep or vertical cracks, and have solidified to form thin curtains of rock known as **dykes**. You will consider dykes in more detail in Chapters 6 and 11.

Activity 1.3 Introducing maps in geology

This activity presents a number of visualisations of basic map concepts, such as scale and topography, which should help you develop confidence in working with topographical and geological maps throughout the course.

1.5 Summary of Chapter 1

1 Among the most important ideas in the early history of geology (and those people most closely associated with them), are the Principle of Superposition (Nicolaus Steno), the Principle of Uniformitarianism (James Hutton), and the Principle of Faunal Succession (William Smith). Sir Charles Lyell brought together and developed these three principles.

2 The scope of geology, an interdisciplinary science, covers an exceptionally wide range of scales of space and time. The processes of geology range from the split-second decay of individual radioactive atoms in a tiny crystal to the slow movement of the Earth's vast tectonic plates over millions of years.

3 Igneous rocks are formed by the cooling and solidification (usually crystallisation) of magma. Sedimentary rocks are formed by the accumulation of sediment that is deposited by water, air or ice. Metamorphic rocks form when rocks of any original type (igneous, sedimentary or metamorphic) are changed by heat and/or pressure.

4 Absolute ages of rocks can be determined by measuring the products of the radioactive decay of certain elements, allowing dates to be assigned to the geological timescale.

5 Geological maps developed from the early ideas of William Smith, who was the first to show the outcrop patterns of strata on a map of Britain.

6   Geological maps generally have a key with a stratigraphic column of sedimentary rocks showing the oldest at the bottom and the youngest at the top. This interrelates the principles of superposition and faunal succession.

7   Igneous and metamorphic rocks are also shown on geological maps and in the keys to those maps.

8   Geological maps necessarily contain an element of interpretation in areas where the exposure of solid rocks is restricted.

9   Geological maps contain information about the rock types, stratigraphic ages and structures of the rocks. Small-scale maps are less detailed than larger-scale maps.

10 Geological and other spatial information can be stored, manipulated and analysed using a computerised Geographical Information System (GIS), a powerful tool for the modern geologist.

1.6   Objectives for Chapter 1

Now you have completed this chapter, you should be able to:

1.1 Locate a feature on any British map using the National Grid.

1.2 Describe the age relationships of the stratigraphic units of the UK using the Bedrock UK Map (North and South sheets).

1.3 State the correct relative ages of rocks in terms of the Eons, Eras and Periods of the stratigraphic column.

1.4 Describe some of the main features of the geology of Britain.

Now try the following questions to test your understanding of Chapter 1.

Question 1.5

Use your Bedrock UK Map (S) to answer the following.

(a) Which town is located at grid reference SU (41) 1330?
(b) What sedimentary rock comprises the bedrock on which the town is built?
(c) To what Era and Period does this rock belong?
(d) Approximately how many million years ago were these sediments laid down?

Question 1.6

On your Bedrock UK Map (N or S sheet), locate the Isle of Man within square SC (24) and note the separate lithostratigraphic column for the Lake District (including the Isle of Man) in the index.

(a) To what Period do the youngest sedimentary rocks on the island belong?
(b) To what Period do the oldest sedimentary rocks on the island belong?
(c) List the Periods represented by sedimentary rocks on the island in chronological order.

Question 1.7

Use the simplified geological map in Figure 1.7 to answer (a) and (b). For (b), you will also need to refer to Figure 1.4.

(a) To which geological Period do the rocks of the northernmost tip of mainland Scotland and the southernmost tip of Ireland belong, and hence what are their approximate ages?

(b) What is the maximum difference in age (in millions of years) between the rocks on which London and Dublin are built?

Chapter 2 Minerals and the crystalline state

2.1 Introduction

As you saw in Section 1.1, rocks are made of minerals and, as minerals are natural crystals, the geological world is mostly a crystalline world. Many large-scale geological processes, such as the movement of continents and the metamorphism of large volumes of rock during mountain building, represent the culmination of microscopic processes occurring inside minerals. An understanding of mineral structures and properties allows us to answer questions such as, 'Why is quartz so hard?' and 'Why is quartz so often the dominant type of sand grain on a beach?' and 'How can solid rocks bend into huge folds, or flow like a liquid over geological time?' Minerals and rocks are also, of course, natural resources that provide the inorganic raw materials for almost everything humans use. A good scientific understanding of their origins, occurrence and properties helps to maximise their potential benefits to humanity. In this course, you will look at mineral and rock specimens in various ways (Box 2.1).

Box 2.1 Mineral and rock specimens in the Home Kit, Digital Kit and Virtual Microscope

In this course, we will often refer to real mineral specimens (MS) and rock specimens (RS) in the Home Kit, as well as to interactive images of minerals and rocks in the Digital Kit and the Virtual Microscope. All the minerals and rocks in the Home Kit are represented by photographs in the Digital Kit, and microscope views of all the rocks in the Home Kit can be seen in the Virtual Microscope. Minerals in the Home Kit are labelled with Roman numerals (e.g. MS VII), and rocks in the Home Kit by numbers (e.g. RS 8). The abbreviations MS and RS are not used in the Digital Kit and the Virtual Microscope, where full names are given. Note that there are more minerals and rocks in the Digital Kit and the Virtual Microscope than in the Home Kit.

As all the Home Kit specimens (MS or RS) are also available on the Digital Kit or Virtual Microscope, reference to each of these latter resources is often omitted after mention of MS or RS. Similarly, to avoid repetition, relevant Home Kit mineral and rock specimens are not mentioned every time their name appears in the text.

As you work through the course, we hope you will use all the materials at your disposal. How you use these materials is up to you, though we feel it is most important that you use the real Home Kit specimens wherever possible, not just those in the Digital Kit and the Virtual Microscope.

Take a look at the granite in Figure 2.1a and examine the granite rock specimen RS 13 in the Home Kit. This rock is composed of three distinct types of crystal, each of which is a different mineral: shiny black *biotite mica*; cloudy *orthoclase feldspar* (MS IX in the Home Kit); translucent grey *quartz* (MS III and MS VII).

The junction between any two adjacent crystals in the rock is called a **grain boundary**. Grain boundaries occur where crystals develop in contact with each other – here, during the cooling and crystallisation of magma to form granite. Grain boundaries also develop when minerals grow in the solid state during metamorphism. Where the crystals form an interlocking mass, as in granite or marble, they rarely have the opportunity to develop good crystal faces. By contrast, the best-formed crystals are often ones that have grown into cracks or cavities (such as a gas bubble in a lava flow). Figure 2.1b shows several such quartz crystals that have grown into a cavity.

(a)

(b)

Figure 2.1　(a) A close-up of a piece of granite, 7 cm across, showing interlocking, intergrown crystals of several different minerals. (b) Well-formed quartz crystals. The largest crystal is 6 cm long.

Crystals may be objects of great beauty, in part because of their almost perfectly flat crystal faces and geometric shapes. This regular external appearance is caused by a highly ordered internal arrangement of atoms, known as the crystal structure, which leads to distinct, and to some extent predictable, physical and chemical properties.

Minerals, by definition, are solid substances (Section 1.1). Before looking at the crystalline world in more detail, the next section considers briefly the various physical states that matter can have, and the transition from one state to another – concepts that remain relevant at various stages throughout the course.

2.2　States of matter

Substances generally exist in one of three different states: as a gas, liquid or solid. Figure 2.2 illustrates these states in terms of their atomic arrangements.

Atoms or molecules in a gas move at high velocities, and the distances between them are large, so gases have low densities. In a liquid, the atomic motions are slower, and the atoms are closer together (producing a higher density). If you could take a snapshot of the atoms in a liquid or a gas, you would see a random or disordered arrangement. Another snapshot, taken a fraction of a second later, would look different. So, the internal structures of liquids and gases are disordered both in space and time.

A kind of real-life snapshot of a liquid structure can be taken by very rapidly cooling the liquid to quench it, so that it solidifies before the atoms have had time to rearrange themselves. At low temperatures, there is not enough thermal energy for the atoms to move relative to each other. The quenched material is a disordered solid, known as an **amorphous** solid or **glass** (Figure 2.2).

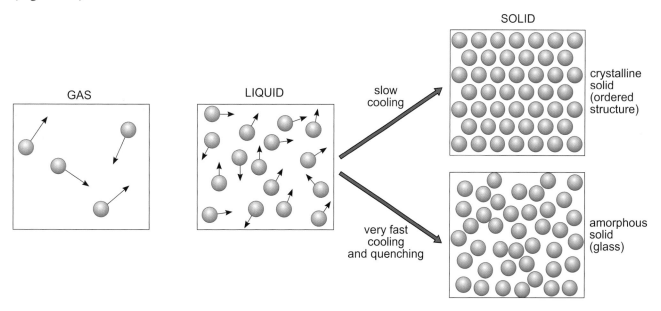

Figure 2.2 Schematic diagrams of atomic arrangements in the gas, liquid and solid states. The small black arrows represent relative velocities of atoms or molecules in the liquid and gas. In a crystalline solid, atoms are confined to specific sites in a regular structure; in a glass, atoms are largely immobile, and the resulting arrangement resembles an instantaneous 'snapshot' of its high-temperature, liquid structure.

By contrast, slow cooling of a liquid allows atoms to arrange themselves into an ordered pattern, which may extend over a huge number of atoms. This kind of solid is called **crystalline**. So if a melt of a given composition (e.g. SiO_2) is cooled very rapidly it will produce a silica glass, whereas if it were cooled slowly it would produce a crystalline solid composed of quartz crystals.

You will encounter examples of naturally formed glass in Chapter 6. It is important to note, however, that compared with crystalline solids, glass is not a particularly stable form of matter. Over many years, glass may slowly convert into a crystalline form in a process called devitrification, and this can sometimes be observed in centuries-old window panes, where circular frosted patches of tiny crystals have formed within the glass.

The states in which a single substance can exist – gas, liquid or solid – are referred to as **phases** of matter. The range of pressures and temperatures over which a particular phase is stable (i.e. its **stability field**) can be shown on a **phase diagram**. The stability fields of different phases may be represented as areas separated by boundary lines on a pressure–temperature diagram, as illustrated in Figure 2.3, a phase diagram for H_2O. A change of temperature (or pressure) may result in a **phase transformation**; for example, liquid H_2O (water) can be heated to form a gas (steam), or cooled to form a solid (ice).

At the surface of the Earth, with a typical pressure of one atmosphere (approximately 10^5 Pa), a crystalline solid, ice, is the stable phase of H_2O at temperatures below 0 °C. Above this temperature (the melting point of ice), solid ice transforms to liquid water. The boundary between the solid and liquid stability fields is a **phase boundary**, and is indicated by a solid line in Figure 2.3. If the temperature continues to increase at constant pressure (along the horizontal dashed line in Figure 2.3), the phase boundary between the liquid (water) stability field and the gas (steam) stability field is reached. This boundary represents the boiling temperature of water. Although only the effect of *changing temperature* has been considered so far, it is important to note that both the melting temperature and the boiling temperature vary with pressure. The point where all three phase boundaries for H_2O meet is called the **triple point**, a unique pressure and temperature where solid (ice), gas (steam) and liquid (water) can coexist.

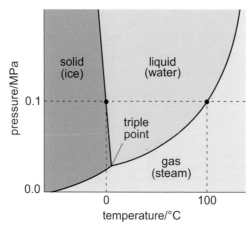

Figure 2.3 A phase diagram for the three phases of H_2O, showing their stability fields over a range of pressures, measured in Pa, and temperatures, measured in °C. (The SI unit of pressure is the pascal, abbreviated to Pa; $1 \text{ Pa} = 1 \text{ N m}^{-2}$; atmospheric pressure is approximately 10^5 Pa, or 0.1 MPa.) The curved lines represent the boundaries between the different stability fields. The dashed lines are guidelines and represent boiling and freezing at atmospheric pressure.

■ How would the boiling temperature of water, measured at the top of a high mountain where the atmospheric pressure is much lower, compare with its boiling temperature at sea level?

☐ The H_2O phase diagram (Figure 2.3) shows that the boiling temperature of water (indicated by the liquid/gas phase boundary) decreases with decreasing pressure. Thus, on top of a mountain, where atmospheric pressure is lower, water boils at a lower temperature.

2.3   Physical properties of minerals in hand specimen

Physical properties, such as colour and density, are those that can be observed without causing any change in the chemical composition of a specimen, whereas chemical properties determine how a substance behaves in a chemical reaction. Many of the physical properties of minerals can be predicted from a detailed knowledge of their crystal structures, which can be obtained by various analytical techniques. Alternatively, physical properties can be used to infer particular aspects of a mineral's internal structure.

Several physical properties of minerals can be readily observed from hand specimens, and can be used for recognising and distinguishing different minerals.

2.3.1   Crystal shape

Well-developed crystals show a number of flat faces and a distinct shape. The shape of the crystal, and the precise arrangement of its crystal faces, relate to its internal structure, and are expressions of the regular way the atoms are arranged.

Many terms are used to describe the shapes of different crystals. These can be broadly grouped into three categories:

- prismatic (the crystal is stretched out in one direction; Figure 2.4a)
- tabular (the crystal is squashed along one direction, so appears slab-like or platy; Figure 2.4b and c)
- equidimensional (the crystal has a rather similar appearance in different directions, e.g. cubes, octahedra, and 'rounded' crystals with many faces of similar size; Figure 2.4d and e).

Crystals of the same mineral tend to show the same general crystal shape. Quartz, for example, is almost always prismatic, rather than tabular or equidimensional. However, the *exact* shape of crystals of the same mineral can vary, depending on the conditions at the time of growth. Two crystals of the same mineral may differ in the relative sizes of specified crystal faces, or some faces may not be present. Although the relative *sizes* of specific crystal faces often vary, the *angles* between such faces are always fixed as they are defined by the crystal structure. This consistency of angles may be verified by measuring the angle between crystal faces with, for example, a protractor (Figure 2.5) or a more accurate device called a goniometer.

Figure 2.4 Some examples of crystal shapes: (a) prismatic (quartz) (6 cm long); (b) tabular (mica) (9 cm across); (c) tabular (barite) (field of view 10 cm across); (d) equidimensional (garnet, MS X) (4 cm); (e) equidimensional (pyrite, MS I) (2 cm).

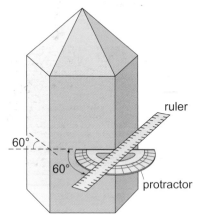

Figure 2.5 Idealised quartz crystal showing that the prism faces are 60° apart. The prism faces may vary in size, but the angles between them are all exactly 60°.

■ Some minerals have a crystal shape that is best described as 'acicular' (i.e. needle-like). In which of the three general categories of crystal shape mentioned above do acicular crystals lie?

☐ Acicular crystals belong to the prismatic category as they are stretched out in one direction.

Note that there is often a distinction between the shape of *individual* crystals and the form they may take when many crystals are assembled into an *aggregate*. For example, some minerals have acicular crystals that radiate in all directions away from a central point, forming a globular (i.e. spherical) aggregate. Aggregates may also be fibrous, columnar, dendritic (clusters of crystals in fern-like branches), and so on. When crystals grow together in a solid mass, in which individual crystals cannot clearly be seen, aggregates are described as massive.

2.3.2 Colour

The colour of a mineral can be its most obvious feature, but colour can also be one of the least reliable properties for identifying minerals. Many minerals show a wide range of coloration, often caused by tiny amounts of impurities. For example, pure quartz (SiO_2) is colourless; minute quantities of Fe^{3+} iron induce a purple coloration, characteristic of the variety of quartz known as amethyst (Figure 2.6a). Small amounts of aluminium cause the dark coloration of smoky quartz when the crystal has been exposed to natural radioactivity (Figure 2.6b). The reason for the pink colour in rose quartz (Figure 2.6c) is not fully understood; titanium or manganese may be involved, as may minute fibrous crystals of a complex mineral within the quartz. The yellow colour of citrine (another quartz variety) is probably due to minute amounts of iron hydrates dispersed within the crystal. (Many examples of citrine for sale are actually artificially heated or irradiated amethyst.) Milky quartz is white and cloudy as a result of tiny bubbles of fluid (liquid and/or gas). In a few minerals, such as tourmaline, an individual crystal may be multicoloured (Figure 2.7), reflecting subtle changes in chemical composition as it grew.

Some minerals do, however, have reliable and distinctive colours. Silicate minerals that contain large amounts of iron are typically dark green or black. These minerals, which often also contain magnesium, are called **ferromagnesian minerals**; they include olivine, pyroxene, amphibole and biotite mica (see Chapter 4).

Figure 2.7 Tourmaline, a complex silicate mineral that shows a variety of colours. Although most commonly black, other colours of tourmaline include brown, green, pink, blue or yellow. Here, a single crystal varies markedly in colour along its length (5 cm). In this case, the green part has the most iron, and the pink colour is due to trace amounts of manganese.

2.3.3 Lustre

The term **lustre** refers to the surface appearance of a mineral, which depends on the way it reflects light. Typical terms used to describe a mineral's lustre include vitreous (rather like glass), metallic and resinous. Quartz (Figure 2.4a) has a vitreous lustre, as do many other silicate minerals, such as feldspar. When transparent, like window glass or clear coloured glass, the term 'glassy' lustre may be used instead of vitreous: quartz, for example, often has a glassy lustre. Some opaque minerals scatter light very strongly, giving rise to shiny, reflective surfaces and a metallic lustre, such as seen in pyrite (MS I), galena (MS VI) and magnetite (Figure 2.8a). Other examples are pearly lustre (looking like pearls) (Figure 2.8b), silky lustre (like shiny threads or fibres)

(a)

(b)

(c)

Figure 2.6 Some coloured varieties of quartz: (a) purple amethyst (crystals 1.5 cm long); (b) grey smoky quartz (5 cm long); (c) pink rose quartz (8.5 cm long). See text for discussion.

(Figure 2.8c), and a dull or earthy lustre (Figure 2.8d). Note that, as in the case of gypsum (Figures 2.8b and c; MS V), different varieties of the same mineral may show different types of lustre.

Figure 2.8 Some examples of lustre: (a) metallic (magnetite) (specimen 4 cm across); (b) pearly (gypsum, variety selenite) (field of view 7 cm across); (c) silky (gypsum, variety satin spar) (5.5 cm); (d) dull or earthy (psilomelane, a form of manganese oxide) (field of view 4.5 cm across).

2.3.4 Cleavage

If a crystal is struck with a hammer, it will probably shatter into many pieces. Some minerals, such as calcite (MS IV, MS XII), break into well-defined blocky shapes with flat surfaces. These are called cleavage fragments (Figure 2.9a and b) and the flat surfaces are called **cleavage planes**. Note that cleavage planes, which occur *within* a crystal, are not the same as crystal faces. **Cleavage** arises when the crystal structure contains repeated parallel planes of weakness (due to weak chemical bonds), along which the crystal will preferentially break. The mineral mica (which includes biotite and muscovite (MS II)) has such perfect cleavage in one direction that it can be readily split, or cleaved, into wafer-thin sheets (Figure 2.9c), using just a fingernail. Some minerals break into irregular fragments that lack flat surfaces (except for any remnants of original crystal faces). In the case of quartz (Figure 2.9d and MS III), which has no cleavage, the broken pieces have a curved fracture pattern, called **conchoidal** (pronounced 'con-koi-dal') fracture. Some minerals have only one set of cleavage planes, others have two sets, and a few (such as calcite) have three. In minerals with only one or two sets of cleavage planes, some broken surfaces will show just fracture.

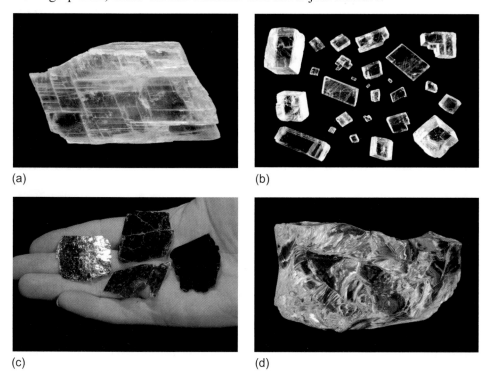

(a) (b)

(c) (d)

Figure 2.9 Aspects of cleavage in minerals. (a) Cleavage planes within a gypsum crystal (11 cm). (b) Cleavage fragments (rhombs) of calcite. Each piece is bounded by three sets of cleavage planes (no two of which intersect at right-angles). The largest fragment is 2 cm long. (c) Biotite (a type of mica), which readily splits along cleavage planes to give very thin sheets. (d) A broken quartz fragment showing an absence of any cleavage planes, and conchoidal fracture (5 cm).

2.3.5 Density

Density is a measure of how heavy an object is for a given volume. You can get a general idea of the relative densities of different minerals just by picking them up: a piece of galena (MS VI) feels heavier than a piece of quartz *of the same size*. The density of a mineral depends on its chemical composition, the type of bonding and its crystal structure. The standard unit of density is kg m^{-3}. Examples of the relative densities of various minerals compared with water at room temperature (about 1000 kg m^{-3}) are shown in Table 2.1. The relationship between density and crystal structure is explored further in Section 2.4.

Table 2.1 Relative densities of various minerals.

Mineral	Symbol/formula	Relative density at room conditions (compared with water = 1.0)
graphite	C	2.2
quartz	SiO_2	2.7
diamond	C	3.5
barite	$BaSO_4$	4.5
galena	PbS	7.6
silver	Ag	10.5
gold	Au	19.3

2.3.6 Hardness

Hardness is loosely defined as the resistance of a material to scratching or indentation. The absolute hardness of a material can be determined precisely, using a mechanical instrument to measure the indentation of a special probe into a crystal surface. However, you can get a general idea of a mineral's *relative* hardness, by undertaking a few simple scratch tests.

Figure 2.10 Three very hard minerals: (a) topaz (5 cm long); (b) corundum (variety ruby) (1 cm); (c) diamond (6 mm).

The 19th century German mineralogist, Friedrich Mohs, devised a useful scale of mineral hardnesses, consisting of well-known minerals, ranked in order of increasing hardness, from talc, with a hardness of 1, to diamond, with a hardness of 10 (Table 2.2). Compared with an absolute hardness scale, **Mohs' scale** is highly non-linear (diamond is about four times harder than corundum; Figure 2.10c and b) but, because the scale uses common minerals, it provides a quick and easy reference for geologists in the field. Minerals with a hardness of less than 2.5 may be scratched by a fingernail, whereas those with a hardness of less than 3.5 may be scratched by a copper coin, and so on.

Table 2.2 Mohs' hardness scale.

Mohs' hardness	Reference mineral	Non-mineral example (hardness in brackets)
1	talc	
2	gypsum	
		fingernail (2.5)
3	calcite	
		copper coin[1] (3.5)
4	fluorite	
5	apatite	
		window glass/ordinary knife blade (5.5)
6	orthoclase feldspar[2]	
		hardened steel (6.5)
7	quartz	
8	topaz	
9	corundum	
10	diamond	

[1] Note that many of today's 'copper coins' are copper-plated steel and are harder below the copper coating.

[2] Other types of feldspar may have a slightly greater hardness, between 6 and 6.5.

■ Will quartz scratch topaz (Figure 2.10a)?

□ The hardness of quartz is 7, whereas topaz has a hardness of 8, so topaz will scratch quartz but not the other way round.

Hardness should not be confused with toughness, which is the resistance of a material to breaking. Many minerals are hard, but they may not be tough. Diamond, for example, is the hardest known material, but it is not tough: it will shatter if dropped onto a hard surface.

Activity 2.1 Physical properties of minerals in the Home Kit

This activity covers the important properties that can be used to distinguish minerals in hand specimen.

2.4 The atomic structure of crystals

The atomic structure of a mineral influences many of its physical and optical properties. This section briefly considers some of the main ways in which atoms are arranged, and how they are bonded, starting with metals, which have some of the simplest atomic arrangements possible. Variations on these arrangements provide the structural foundations of many common minerals.

2.4.1 Metallic structures and bonding

Metal crystals are built from layers of densely packed metal **cations** (atoms that have lost one or more electrons, leaving them positively charged). The ions are organised in regular, *close-packed* arrangements. In close-packing, a layer of identically sized atoms (or ions) occupies the minimum possible space – like a raft of hard spheres (e.g. marbles) in contact with each other. Each atom has six neighbours in a plane. The three-dimensional structure of a metal involves the successive stacking of close-packed layers on top of each other.

In metallic bonding, atoms donate one or more outer electrons to a free electron 'sea' (Figure 2.11a), which flows between and around the cations and acts as a kind of glue, holding them together. This kind of bonding is uniform in all directions, so that **metallic structures** are dense and close-packed. The electron mobility renders metals both malleable and ductile, which are vital properties for producing thin sheets and for stretching out to form thin cables or filaments (e.g. copper wire).

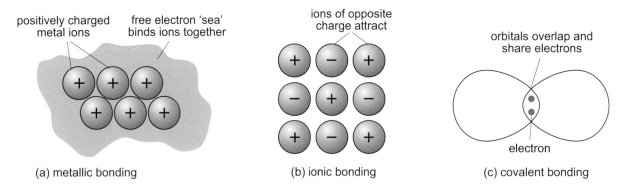

Figure 2.11 Schematic representation of three types of chemical bonding: (a) metallic bonding; (b) ionic bonding; (c) covalent bonding.

2.4.2 Ionic structures and bonding

About 90% of all minerals are essentially ionic compounds. An ionic bond is generated by the *transfer* of one or more electrons from one atom to another. This creates two ions of opposite charge, which are attracted to each other (Figure 2.11b). For example, in **halite** (sodium chloride, NaCl) there is a positively charged sodium cation, Na^+, and a negatively charged chlorine **anion**, Cl^-. As with metallic bonding, ionic bonds are non-directional, so ionic crystals tend to have fairly dense, close-packed structures. However, ionic bonds tend to be stronger than metallic bonds, so crystals containing ionic bonds tend to be unmalleable and much more brittle than metal crystals.

Even though a close-packed structure looks densely packed, there are actually lots of spaces between the atoms. These spaces are called **interstices** and are important in metallic structures because they provide sites for smaller atoms to reside. Interstices also provide a basis for many **ionic structures**: they provide locations for smaller ions, in the presence of large ions. There are two kinds of interstices: a tetrahedral interstice, surrounded by four atoms, one at each of the corners of an imaginary tetrahedron (Figure 2.12a); and an octahedral interstice, surrounded by six atoms, arranged at the corners of an imaginary octahedron (Figure 2.12b).

TETRAHEDRAL INTERSTICE

(hidden) interstice
lies between four atoms

OCTAHEDRAL INTERSTICE

interstice lies
between six atoms

(a)

(b)

Figure 2.12 Interstices (vacant sites) between two close-packed planes of spheres. (a) A tetrahedral interstice is formed between four close-packed atoms (three in the lower layer and one in the upper layer). The atoms are arranged at the corners of a tetrahedron (schematic figure on the right), with the interstice at its centre. (b) An octahedral interstice is formed between six close-packed atoms (three in each layer). The atoms are arranged at the corners of an octahedron (schematic figure), with the interstice at its centre.

The mineral halite (Figure 2.13) is an example of a structure with octahedral interstices (as in Figure 2.12b). The chlorine ions are arranged a bit like the atoms in a metal – although they do not quite touch each other. The sodium ions, which are much smaller, fit snugly between the large chlorine ions, as illustrated in a space-filling model (Figure 2.13a).

The structure of **sphalerite** (zinc sulfide, ZnS) (Figure 2.14) has a close-packed arrangement of sulfur ions, a structure in which zinc ions fill half of the tetrahedral interstices (as in Figure 2.12a).

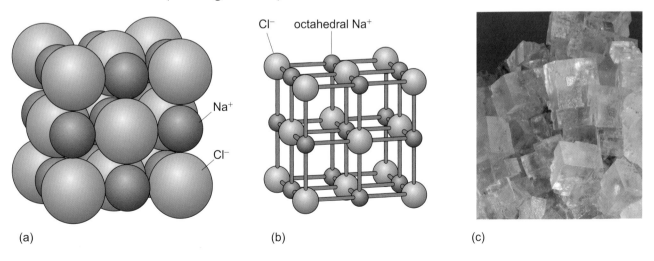

Cl⁻   octahedral Na⁺

Na⁺

Cl⁻

(a)

(b)

(c)

Figure 2.13 The structure of halite (sodium chloride, NaCl): (a) a space-filling model (sodium and chlorine ions shown at their correct relative sizes); (b) a ball-and-stick model. (c) Cubic crystals of halite (field of view 10 cm across).

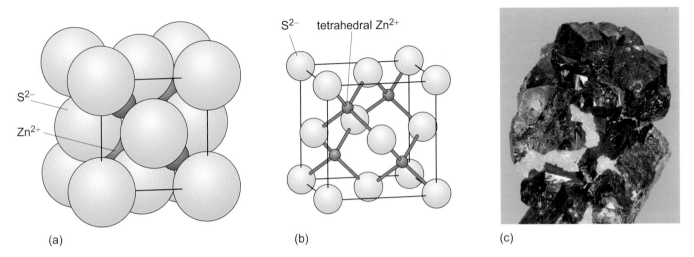

Figure 2.14 Structure of sphalerite (zinc sulfide, ZnS): (a) a space-filling model; (b) ball-and-stick model; the unit cell (see Section 2.6) is shown by black lines in both (a) and (b). (c) Sphalerite (with white quartz) (2 cm across).

2.4.3 Covalent structures and bonding

A covalent bond is formed when two atoms *share* two electrons, through overlap and merging of two electron orbitals, one from each atom (Figure 2.11c). Crystals containing covalent bonds tend to have more complex structures than those of ionic or metallic structures. Covalent bonding requires the *precise overlap* of electron orbitals, so if an atom forms several covalent bonds, these are usually constrained to specific directions. As covalent bonds are directional, unlike metallic or ionic bonds, this places additional constraints on the arrangements of atoms within such a crystal. One result is that **covalent structures** tend to be more open – and hence have lower densities than metallic or ionic structures.

Diamond is an example of a covalently bonded solid. In this form of carbon, each atom is covalently bonded to four other carbon atoms, arranged at the corners of a tetrahedron (Figure 2.15a). The resulting structure, which has a repeating cubic shape, is illustrated in Figure 2.15b. The structure contains much more unoccupied space than close-packed metal structures.

Another form of solid carbon with covalent bonding is **graphite**. Unlike those in diamond, the carbon atoms in graphite are covalently bonded to *three* neighbours in the same plane (Figure 2.16a), producing a strong sheet of carbon atoms. However, each carbon atom has one extra electron available for bonding that forms very weak bonds, which serve to keep the carbon sheets together (Figure 2.16b).

■ How do the crystal structures of diamond and graphite account for the differences in hardness between the two minerals?

☐ Diamond has a three-dimensional bonding pattern, with identical bonding in all directions, and no 'weak' directions. Graphite has a mainly two-dimensional pattern, with sheets of C–C bonds. Bonds between the sheets are very weak, so sheets can easily slide past each other, explaining graphite's use as a lubricant and why it is soft enough to mark paper.

Diamond and graphite have the same chemical composition (pure carbon) but different crystal structures. They are known as **polymorphs** of carbon. Diamond is formed under higher pressures than graphite (Figure 2.15c), and is less stable than graphite at the surface of the Earth. However, because of the strong bonding, it is very difficult to break down the diamond structure, so diamonds (fortunately) will not spontaneously transform into graphite! Note that not only is diamond harder than graphite, but it is also denser, as predicted by its structure (Table 2.3).

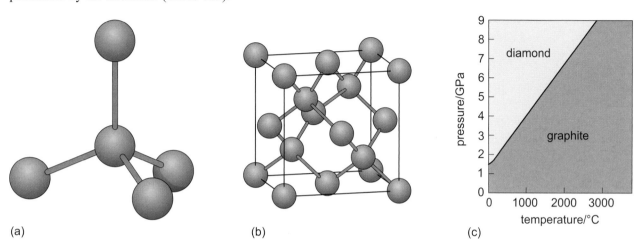

(a) (b) (c)

Figure 2.15 The diamond structure: (a) the tetrahedral arrangement of covalent bonds around a carbon atom; (b) the arrangement of carbon atoms and bonds in the unit cell (see Section 2.6); the unit cell is shown by black lines. (c) Phase diagram illustrating the stability fields for graphite and diamond. Temperature and pressure conditions within the Earth are such that diamond tends to form only at depths greater than 150 km.

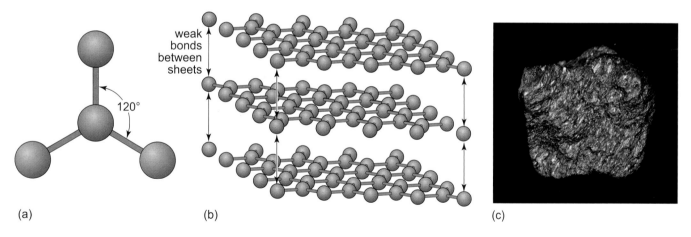

(a) (b) (c)

Figure 2.16 The graphite structure: (a) the triangular arrangement of covalent bonds around a carbon atom in the same plane; (b) part of the three-dimensional structure of graphite, showing strongly bonded hexagonal sheets of carbon atoms, connected by weak bonds. (c) Specimen of graphite (3.5 cm across).

Table 2.3 Relative densities of various minerals and ice, and notes on their structure and bonding.

Substance	Relative density at room conditions (compared with water = 1.0)	Structure and bonding
ice, H_2O	0.9	open structure; covalent bonds plus weak bonds between H_2O molecules
graphite, C	2.2	open structure; covalent bonds plus weak bonds between layers
feldspar, $KAlSi_3O_8$	2.5	open structure; predominantly covalent bonds
quartz, SiO_2	2.7	open structure; predominantly covalent bonds
olivine, Mg_2SiO_4–Fe_2SiO_4	3.2–4.4	structure based on close-packing, but with ionic and covalent bonds. Density increases as Fe content increases
diamond, C	3.5	structure based on close-packing, but with covalent bonds
barite, $BaSO_4$	4.5	ionic bonds between barium and sulfate groups
hematite (iron oxide), Fe_2O_3	5.3	structure based on close-packing; ionic and metallic bonds
galena (lead sulfide), PbS	7.6	structure based on close-packing; ionic and metallic bonds
silver, Ag	10.5	close-packed structure; metallic bonds
gold, Au	19.3	close-packed structure; metallic bonds

Minerals are never chemically pure; they always contain some foreign atoms. These impurity atoms may simply squeeze into the interstices. Another possibility is that certain elements may be able to directly replace (substitute for) the normal atoms in the ideal structure – although, for a comfortable fit, the substituting element must have a similar size and charge to the original atom. This phenomenon is called **ionic substitution**. An example is the substitution of Fe^{2+} for Mg^{2+}, or Mg^{2+} for Fe^{2+}, which occurs in the mineral olivine (Section 4.3.1).

2.5 Crystal defects and twinning

Virtually all crystals contain minute imperfections or defects. The effect of defects on the physical and chemical properties of a crystal can be out of all proportion to their size. Defects come in several types. *Point defects* may involve missing or displaced atoms in the crystal structure, giving empty sites, or vacancies. Such defects make it much easier for atoms to diffuse through the crystal structure, by moving between vacant sites. This is important because the rate of diffusion of atoms through a crystal lattice can determine the speed at which processes such as weathering, or other chemical reactions (e.g. during metamorphism), will proceed.

Minerals in deformed rocks, such as those from mountain belts, contain large numbers of *line defects* caused by rows of atoms that are out of place in the crystal structure. Figure 2.17 shows an artificial example. Such defects affect the mechanical strength of a crystal, which determines the strength of rocks and how they deform under intense pressure. During deformation, progressive movement along flaws in crystals takes place in tiny steps, as bonds are broken and re-formed.

Figure 2.17 Transmission electron microscope image showing many line defects in a crystal of indium aluminium arsenide (an alloy used in semiconductors). Each dark line represents a strained part of the crystal. The width of this image is about 1 μm.

A third type of defect is called a *planar defect*. Crystals grow by the progressive addition of atoms onto a surface. 'Mistakes' in the stacking of new planes with respect to previously formed planes are common during crystal growth. These planar defects can have a profound effect on the way atoms are stacked, and can produce distinct regions called *domains* within a single crystal. One such planar defect is a boundary that separates two domains of a crystal that are mirror images (Figure 2.18a). The result is called a twinned crystal. Various types of crystal **twinning** exist, and in each case a single crystal consists of two or more regions in which the crystal lattice is differently orientated. The different regions of the twinned crystal may be related in various ways, such as by reflection in a mirror plane or by rotation about a symmetry axis (see Section 2.6). Twinning is especially common in feldspar. Orthoclase feldspar often displays *simple twinning*, in which the crystal is divided into two domains with a different structural orientation (MS VIII; Figure 2.18b and d). Other types of feldspar (e.g. plagioclase feldspar) may have a more complex type of twinning, called *multiple twinning*, in which a single crystal has many different domains (Figure 2.18c).

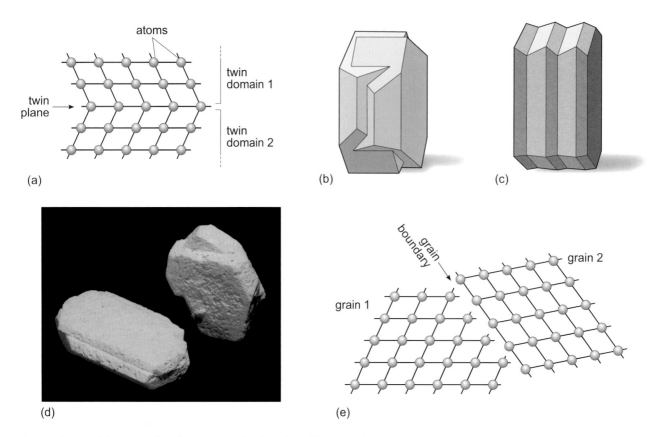

Figure 2.18 (a) Example of crystal twinning, in which a twin plane separates two regions of a single crystal that are mirror images. The two regions are referred to as twin domains. (b) An example of simple twinning. (c) An example of multiple twinning. (d) Two crystals of orthoclase feldspar showing simple twinning. The left-hand one is 5 cm long. (e) Grain boundaries are different from twin boundaries because there is no orientation relationship between crystals on either side of the grain boundary. There are two distinct grains, with the same, or a different, mineral composition.

2.6 Crystal symmetry and shape

In this section, you will investigate the relationship between the shape and symmetry of crystals, consider why minerals have only a limited number of crystal shapes, and discover how the shape of a mineral relates to its internal structure.

2.6.1 Crystal symmetry

When you first look at a collection of minerals in a museum, there may seem to be an infinite variety of crystal shapes. However, on closer inspection there is an underlying order, and this is best seen by the consistency in the angles between crystal faces for particular groups of minerals. Crystals possess a variety of symmetries, and it has been demonstrated by X-ray methods that symmetry visible in hand specimen relates to the internal arrangement of atoms.

Most people have an idea of what is meant by symmetry, as many everyday objects and living things possess it. There are two main types of symmetry:

- **reflection symmetry** where one side of an object is the mirror image of the other side (e.g. insects, birds and spoons)
- **rotational symmetry** where an object looks the same after a certain amount of rotation (e.g. many flowers, starfish and bicycle wheels).

Many complicated patterns such as carpet or wallpaper designs have symmetry, but these can sometimes be a little difficult to discern. Consider, for example, an object with obvious symmetry, such as a snowflake (Figure 2.19). Each snowflake can be rotated by 60° about an axis perpendicular to the page and it will look exactly the same as it did before. The operation can be repeated six times in a full 360° rotation of the page, and at each 60° interval the snowflake will look the same. Thus the snowflake has a six-fold rotational symmetry. A snowflake also possesses reflection symmetry; if you 'split' the snowflakes along certain planes, called **mirror planes**, the two halves are mirror images of each other. Some examples of rotational and reflection symmetry found in crystals are illustrated in Figure 2.20.

Figure 2.19 Some examples of snowflakes, displaying perfect six-fold rotational symmetry.

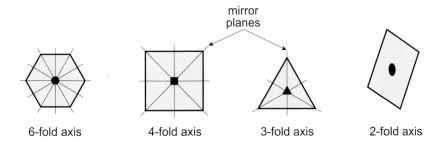

mirror planes

6-fold axis   4-fold axis   3-fold axis   2-fold axis

Figure 2.20 Examples of rotational and reflection symmetries shown by crystals. The first three shapes are bisected with examples of mirror planes to illustrate reflection symmetry. Placed at the centre of each shape is the appropriate symbol for the rotation axis.

2.6.2 Crystal lattices and unit cells

A typical crystal contains billions of atoms in a highly ordered structural arrangement. Perhaps, surprisingly, the essence of such a complex structure can be described relatively simply. How is this possible?

If you tried to tile a two-dimensional area such as a bathroom floor without any gaps, you would do this by adding tiles that fitted together. In fact, only tiles with two-, three- four- and six-fold symmetry allow for successful tiling (Figure 2.21). Similarly, if you tried to produce a three-dimensional structure (like a crystal) without any gaps it would require the repetition of building blocks (i.e. 3D repeating units) with particular shapes. As with two-dimensional tiling, the only kinds of rotational symmetry axis possible in three-dimensional crystals are two-, three-, four- and six-fold axes.

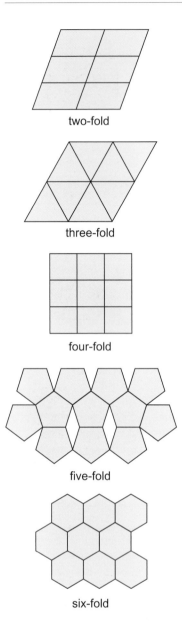

Figure 2.21 Two-dimensional tiling. Some shapes cannot be tiled without gaps appearing. Only two-, three-, four- and six-fold symmetry are consistent with periodic repetition without gaps.

A **lattice** is an array of objects or points that form a periodically repeating pattern in two or three dimensions. In a crystal lattice, the repeating pattern is simply an arrangement of atoms (or ions) that is located at regular points, called lattice points.

Figure 2.22a shows a three-dimensional lattice, the building of which can be envisaged by simply stacking a series of identical two-dimensional lattices on top of each other. A crystal is, in effect, a structure formed by countless numbers of identical tiny building blocks, called **unit cells** (Figure 2.22b), and these make up the crystal lattice. Each mineral has a specific unit cell, which is defined according to the lengths of its sides and their angular relationships. Each unit cell contains one or more different kinds of atoms joined to each other by chemical bonds. Shapes of unit cells vary from one mineral to another; all have six sides (three sets of parallel faces, though not necessarily perpendicular to each other).

To define the resulting three-dimensional lattice, it is convenient to specify reference directions, x, y and z, which are chosen to be parallel to three edges of the unit cell (Figure 2.22b). These are known as **crystallographic axes**, and it is important to realise that they are not always at 90° to each other. The angles between the axes are denoted by the Greek letters α, β and γ (alpha, beta and gamma), as shown in Figure 2.22c. The size of the unit cell is given by the lengths of the three edges, a, b and c, as shown in Figure 2.22b. The unit cell is extremely small – typically less than 1 nm (10^{-9} m) in any direction. It is therefore a huge jump in scale from a single unit cell to a single crystal visible to the naked eye. With an edge length of 1 nm, a crystal only 1 mm^3 requires 10^{18} unit cells to build it: a vast number.

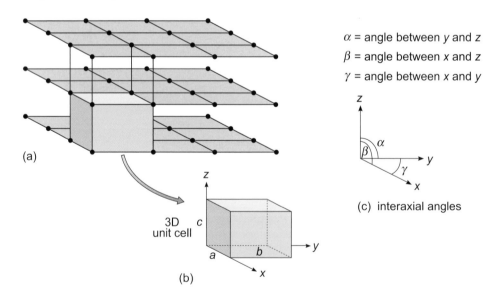

α = angle between y and z
β = angle between x and z
γ = angle between x and y

(c) interaxial angles

Figure 2.22 Anatomy of a three-dimensional lattice. (a) Stacking two-dimensional lattices results in a three-dimensional lattice made of tiny 3D building blocks. (b) The 3D unit cell is the basic building block of the crystal lattice. Its shape is defined in terms of the lengths of the sides and the angles between them. (c) Angles between the three crystallographic axes.

A three-dimensional lattice (which may have billions of lattice points) can be represented by just six numbers: the lattice parameters a, b, c, α, β and γ. In the next section, you will see how the shape of the unit cell relates to a crystal's symmetry, and what this means for the external shapes of crystals.

2.6.3 Crystal systems

Most three-dimensional lattices display some symmetry, although the symmetry elements (e.g. rotation axes and mirror planes) can be in any direction. Some arrangements of symmetry elements place special constraints on the shape of the unit cell. For example, a four-fold rotation axis requires the unit cell to have a square section at right angles to the symmetry axis (Figure 2.23a). Three four-fold axes at right angles to each other imply that the unit cell must be a cube, and so on.

Crystals are classified on the basis of this three-dimensional symmetry (and hence the shapes of their unit cells) into one of seven different **crystal systems** (Figure 2.24).

The beauty of crystallography is that you do not need to see the lattice, the unit cell, or the atoms in order to deduce this symmetry. The extent of symmetry varies from the cubic system, which has the most symmetry, to triclinic, which has the least. Generally, the more symmetry a crystal has, the more constraints this places on its external shape. Crystals belonging to the cubic system tend to have equidimensional shapes, such as cubes, octahedra (with eight faces), or rather rounded-looking crystals with many faces (e.g. dodecahedra, with twelve faces). Pyrite and galena, for example, can have very simple cube-shaped crystals, which clearly indicate their underlying cubic symmetry. These same minerals may also have more complex shapes, with many more faces, but each shape still has the symmetry that places the mineral within the cubic system. The same possibility for variation within certain limits applies to other minerals in different crystal systems. Despite their complexity, by focusing on the symmetry relationships between faces, you may still be able to determine the crystal system.

Sometimes a crystal has less symmetry than first appearance suggests. For example, quartz crystals are usually prismatic, and often have a hexagonal appearance in cross-section (MS VII). At first, quartz thus appears to have a six-fold rotation axis. However, in some well-developed quartz crystals there are a number of small faces that present the same appearance only three times in a full 360° rotation, revealing that the true symmetry is less.

■ Given this information, to which crystal system does quartz belong?

□ The trigonal system (Figure 2.24), as this is the only system in which only one three-fold axis is present.

It is important to realise that conditions during the growth of a crystal often prevent some faces from developing as perfectly as they might, which results in individual crystal faces having different sizes. Some crystal faces may not be developed at all. Therefore, when looking at crystal symmetry, the *angles* between faces should be considered (see Figure 2.5), not the absolute sizes of individual faces.

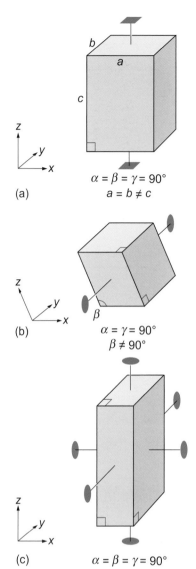

(a) $\alpha = \beta = \gamma = 90°$ $a = b \neq c$

(b) $\alpha = \gamma = 90°$ $\beta \neq 90°$

(c) $\alpha = \beta = \gamma = 90°$

Figure 2.23 Symmetry and shape of some unit cells corresponding with certain rotation axes (reflection planes are not shown): (a) a four-fold rotation axis requires that the crystallographic axes are at 90° to each other, and that the unit cell has a square cross-section; (b) a single two-fold rotation axis as shown constrains two of the crystallographic axes to be at 90° to each other; (c) three two-fold rotation axes at 90° to one another imply that the three crystallographic axes are also at 90° to each other.

Crystal system	Unit cell		Essential symmetry	Example of everyday object with essential symmetry	Mineral example
triclinic	$a \neq b \neq c$ $\alpha \neq \beta \neq \gamma$	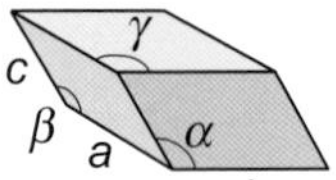	none	a packet of envelopes pushed askew in two directions	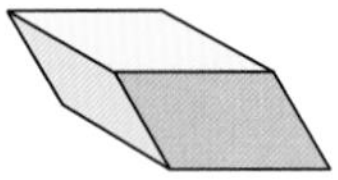 plagioclase feldspar, kyanite
monoclinic	$a \neq b \neq c$ $\alpha = \gamma = 90° \neq \beta$	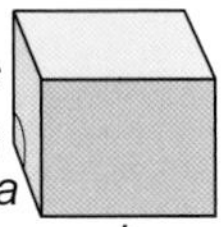	one two-fold axis	a partially squashed matchbox cover, flattened to one side	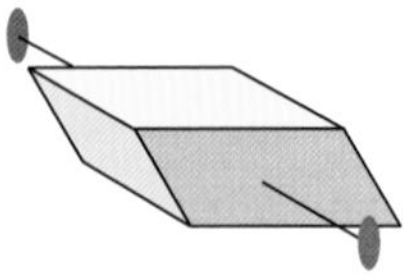 gypsum, biotite mica, muscovite mica, orthoclase feldspar, hornblende (amphibole), augite (pyroxene), talc
orthorhombic	$a \neq b \neq c$ $\alpha = \beta = \gamma = 90°$		three two-fold axes (at 90° to each other)	a matchbox	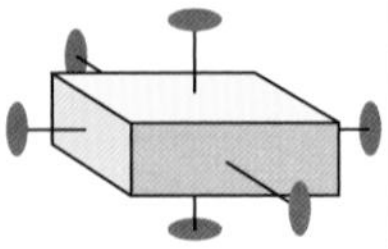 barite, topaz, olivine, andalusite
tetragonal	$a = b \neq c$ $\alpha = \beta = \gamma = 90°$	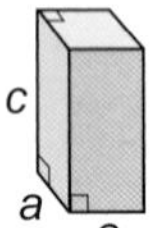	one four-fold axis	two sugar cubes stuck together	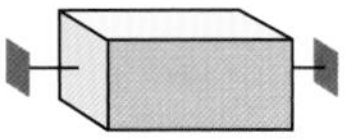 chalcopyrite, zircon
cubic	$a = b = c$ $\alpha = \beta = \gamma = 90°$	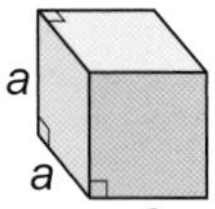	four three-fold axes (through corners)	a sugar cube	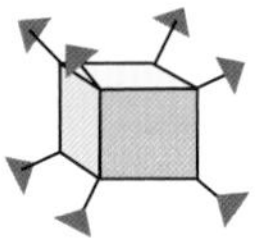 galena, halite, pyrite, fluorite, garnet, diamond, sphalerite, magnetite, silver, gold
trigonal	$a = b = c$ $120° > \alpha = \beta = \gamma \neq 90°$	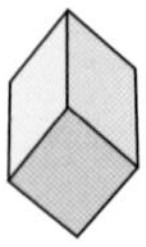	one three-fold axis	a 'Toblerone' packet	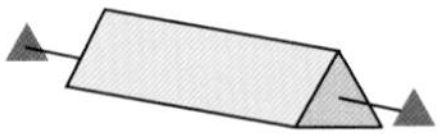 calcite, tourmaline, hematite, corundum (e.g. ruby, sapphire)
hexagonal	$a = b \neq c$ $\alpha = \beta = 90°$ $\gamma = 120°$	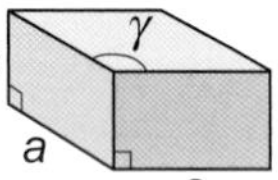	one six-fold axis	unsharpened pencil	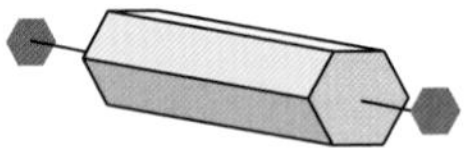 graphite, apatite, beryl (e.g. emerald, aquamarine)

Figure 2.24 Illustration of the seven crystal systems in relation to some everyday objects, and mineral examples. Note that only the diagnostic axes of symmetry have been shown – there are many others, as well as numerous mirror planes. The trigonal system is closely related to the hexagonal system, and is sometimes considered a subsystem of it. All the minerals mentioned in this chapter (except quartz) are given, along with a few others.

Question 2.1

(a) Study the three unit cell shapes shown in Figure 2.23. To which of the seven crystal systems would each belong?

(b) What would be the shape of the cross-section, at right angles to the longest side, of a crystal with a unit cell like that in Figure 2.23a?

Activity 2.2   Introduction to the Digital Kit

This activity is designed to familiarise you with the operation and content of the Digital Kit, which provides access to images and information about the mineral and rock specimens used in this course. Most of the rocks and many of the minerals are also available in the Home Kit.

Activity 2.3   Exploring other minerals in the Digital Kit

This activity uses the Digital Kit to explore the properties of various minerals that are not in the Home Kit.

2.7   Summary of Chapter 2

1 Matter exists in the form of gases, liquids and solids, and the arrangement of atoms becomes progressively more ordered from gases to solids. The stability fields for the three states of a chemical element or compound are shown in a pressure–temperature plot known as a phase diagram.

2 Physical characteristics of minerals evident in hand specimen include crystal shape, colour, lustre, cleavage, density and hardness. Colour may be misleading, as minute amounts of impurities can affect the colour of some minerals. Cleavage, density and hardness are strongly related to the underlying atomic structure.

3 Atoms are bonded together by three different mechanisms: metallic bonding in which a 'sea' of electrons holds the metal cations strongly together, giving dense, closely packed structures; ionic bonding where electrons are transferred between atoms, producing positive and negative ions that are strongly attracted to each other; and covalent bonding where electrons are shared, resulting in open, low-density crystal structures, which are strongly bonded. About 90% of all minerals are essentially ionic compounds.

4 Crystals may have several different types of defect that can strongly influence the mineral's physical and chemical properties.

5 Many geological processes – rock formation, rock deformation, weathering and metamorphism – are controlled by processes operating at much smaller scales, such as the movement of atoms in crystals (diffusion), the breaking of atomic bonds within crystal structures, the initiation and growth of new crystals and phase transformations.

6 Various types of crystal twinning exist, and in each case the twin is a single crystal that consists of two or more regions in which the crystal lattice is differently orientated.

7 The external shape of a crystal (i.e. the arrangement of crystal faces) is controlled by its internal structure. Crystals are composed of atoms arranged in repeating patterns that can have two-, three-, four- or six-fold symmetry. Each repeating pattern is located at a lattice point. A three-dimensional crystal lattice is a structure formed by countless numbers of identical tiny building blocks, called unit cells. Unit cells have a box shape, which can be defined by the length of the three sides of the unit cell (a, b and c) and the angle between the axes of the unit cell (α, β and γ). Variation in the shape of the unit cell results in different symmetry elements (rotation axes and reflection planes), but *all* crystals may be ascribed to one of seven crystal systems.

8 When looking at crystal symmetry, the *angles* between faces are more important to consider than the absolute sizes of individual faces, as conditions during the growth of a crystal often prevent some faces from developing as perfectly as they might, or from developing at all.

2.8   Objectives for Chapter 2

Now you have completed this chapter, you should be able to:

2.1 Give, with an appropriate example, the meaning of the terms phase, phase boundary, and phase transformation, and interpret stability fields in terms of pressures and/or temperatures, using a phase diagram.

2.2 Describe and recognise, giving examples, various physical properties of minerals, including lustre, cleavage, hardness and density.

2.3 Describe, giving mineral examples, the main differences between metallic, ionic and covalent structures and their type of bonding.

2.4 Explain the significance of various types of defects in crystals.

2.5 Explain the meaning of the terms lattice, unit cell, reflection and rotational symmetry, and how these relate to crystal systems.

Now try the following questions to test your understanding of Chapter 2.

Question 2.2

Using the phase diagram illustrated in Figure 2.3, determine: (a) the pressure at which water would boil at a temperature of 50 °C; and (b) the pressure and temperature at which solid ice, liquid water and gaseous steam could coexist.

Question 2.3

On testing, an unidentified mineral was found to scratch window glass, but was itself scratched by a hardened steel file. What is the hardness of this mineral?

Chapter 3   Minerals and the microscope

Although modern Earth Sciences departments use expensive and sophisticated electronic equipment to study minerals and rocks, the polarising microscope (which was the height of instrumental sophistication in the later 19th and early 20th centuries) remains an important tool in **petrology** (the study of rocks). This chapter gives an overview of crystal optics, a basic understanding of which is essential for use of the polarising microscope in **petrography** (the description of rocks). By identifying minerals and examining their interrelationships, petrographic evidence can be used to identify rocks and deduce how they formed.

3.1   The nature of light

Light is a form of **electromagnetic radiation**, but it is only a small part (the visible part) of the whole electromagnetic spectrum, which also includes X-rays, ultraviolet and infrared radiation, and microwaves (Figure 3.1). The wavelengths of visible light span the region of the electromagnetic spectrum from about 400 nm (violet) to about 700 nm (red). Some of the properties of waves, with which you may already be familiar, are summarised in Box 3.1.

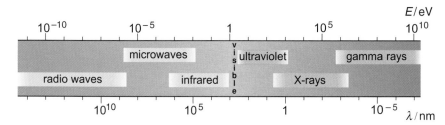

Figure 3.1   The electromagnetic spectrum. Note that wavelength, λ, *decreases* from left to right, but wave energy, E, *increases* in the same direction.

Box 3.1   Revision of waves

A wave is a disturbance that travels through a medium, transporting energy, but without permanent displacement of the medium. A wave moves by oscillations, which may be described as a regular sequence of peaks and troughs (like spreading ripples on a pond). The number of wave peaks that pass a fixed point per second is the frequency; and the distance between successive peaks is the wavelength (Figure 3.2). The wavelength depends on the frequency of the oscillation and the speed of propagation of the wave, according to the relationship:

$$\text{wavelength} = \frac{\text{speed}}{\text{frequency}} \qquad (3.1)$$

The speed of a wave depends on the nature of the medium through which it travels – so, for example, the speed of sound in air is different from its speed in water.

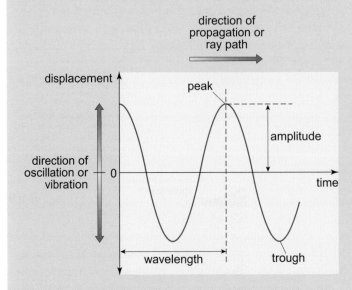

Figure 3.2   A representation of a simple wave as a function of displacement and time.

3.1.1   Colour

Probably the most obvious property of a mineral is its colour. 'White' light contains a range of visible wavelengths from red to violet, but the mixture of colours is perceived to be white. When white light falls on an object some wavelengths are reflected, some are absorbed. The object then appears to be a particular colour because those absorbed wavelengths are missing from the reflected spectrum. The same happens when light passes through an object, which is the case with transparent and translucent minerals. A given crystal absorbs a particular range of wavelengths so that the colour of the light emerging from it depends on the type of mineral it is.

3.1.2   Refraction

When light passes from one transparent medium to another of different density, its speed changes. This effect is known as **refraction**. It is the reason that a straight stick emerging from water appears bent at the surface of the water, and why water viewed from above appears shallower than it really is. The change in the speed of light between air and the medium, expressed as a ratio, is the **refractive index** of the medium. (Note that this is a simplification. Strictly, refractive index is defined as the ratio of the speed of light in a *vacuum* to its speed in the medium. However, the speed of light in air is very close to that in a vacuum.)

3.2   Minerals and polarised light

A beam of light from an ordinary source, such as the Sun, consists of electromagnetic waves that vibrate in all directions at 90° to its direction of travel (Figure 3.3). Such a beam of unpolarised light can be modified to constrain its vibration direction to a single plane by using a polarising filter (a transparent sheet branded as Polaroid). Light transmitted through this polarising filter (or **polariser**) is called **plane-polarised light** (Figure 3.3). The direction of polarisation is the **permitted vibration direction** of the material. This effect is the basis for various observations using the polarising microscope that are important for identifying minerals.

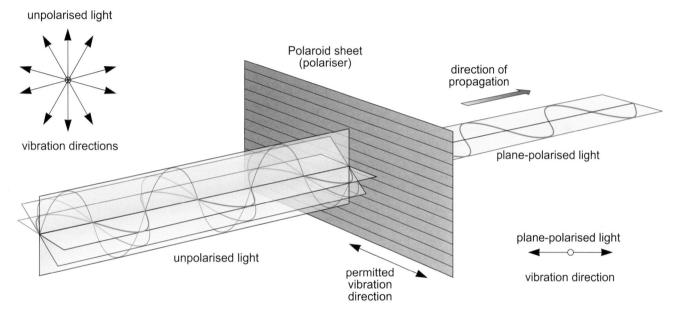

Figure 3.3   The production of plane-polarised light using a polarising filter.

3.2.1   Isotropic and anisotropic materials

Materials that have the same atomic structure in all directions are termed **isotropic**. When light passes through such a material it doesn't matter in which direction the light vibrates, its speed (and therefore the refractive index) is the same. This is true of light passing through air, water, glass and some minerals.

■   To which crystal system would you expect an isotropic mineral to belong?

☐   The cubic system, because it defines materials for which the crystal structure and, consequently, its optical properties are the same along each crystallographic axis.

Minerals belonging to other crystal systems are more common than those with cubic symmetry. They have internal structures that are not the same along all crystallographic axes and are therefore **anisotropic** minerals. The importance of this is that the behaviour of the light passing through an anisotropic crystal depends on the vibration direction of the light and its relationship to the crystal structure.

3.2.2 Double refraction

Anisotropic crystals have a remarkable property: when plane-polarised light enters such a crystal, it splits into two rays. The explanation for this involves complex crystal physics, which is well beyond the scope of this course. Nevertheless, the consequences are profound. The two rays are each plane-polarised, but their planes of polarisation (i.e. their vibration directions) are at 90° to each other. This means that each ray encounters a different atomic arrangement and therefore travels at a different speed through the crystal – so they have different refractive indices. The difference in refractive index of the two rays is called **birefringence**. If the refractive indices are very different (i.e. the crystal has a very high birefringence), then the two rays will be refracted to very different extents, and it may be possible to view two distinct images through the crystal, one for each ray. This effect, called **double refraction**, can be seen in the transparent variety of calcite, Iceland spar (Figure 3.4 and MS XII), and is the subject of Activity 3.1.

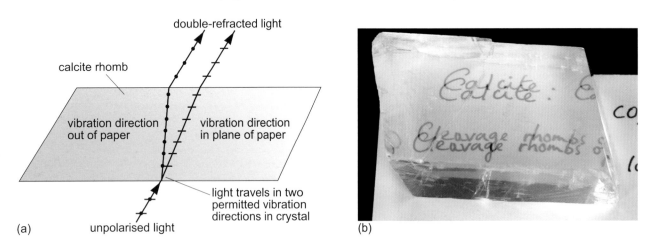

(a)   (b)

Figure 3.4 (a) Side-view through a calcite cleavage rhomb, showing how light is doubly refracted into two rays as it passes through the crystal. For calcite, the refractive indices (or speeds) of the two rays are very different, so they travel along quite different paths through the crystal. (b) Double refraction in natural calcite (Iceland spar). The difference in the speeds (i.e. refractive indices) of the two rays is so great that the eye perceives two images.

■   Would you expect to see double refraction in a cubic crystal?

☐   No. Cubic crystals are isotropic. Double refraction occurs only in anisotropic crystals.

Activity 3.1   Calcite rhomb experiment

In this activity, you will observe double refraction in an Iceland spar cleavage rhomb (MS XII) and investigate the polarisation of the two light rays emerging from the crystal.

3.2.3   Pleochroism

When plane-polarised light passes through an isotropic crystal, where the properties of the crystal are the same in all crystallographic directions, the colour of the transmitted light (due to the absorption characteristics of the crystal, Section 3.1.1) doesn't change as the crystal is rotated. However, when plane-polarised light passes through some, but not all, anisotropic crystals, and splits (Section 3.2.2), the light interacts with different arrangements of atoms with different absorption characteristics as the crystal is rotated, thus affecting the crystal's colour. As an example, Figure 3.5a shows a very thin slice of biotite (a common rock-forming mineral) which has a faint beige colour when viewed in plane-polarised light and the cleavage is north–south. On rotating the mineral through 90°, the colour gradually changes to deep brown when the cleavage is east–west (Figure 3.5b). The same effects are repeated in Figures 3.5c and d. This property, whereby the colour of a mineral varies on rotation in plane-polarised light, is called **pleochroism**.

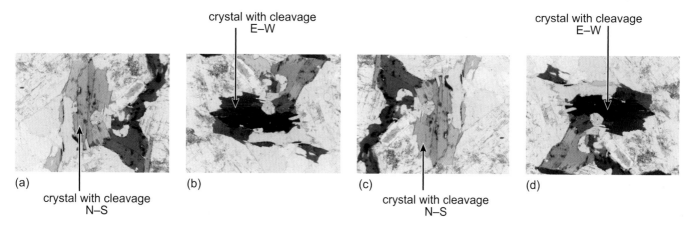

crystal with cleavage
E–W

crystal with cleavage
E–W

(a)   (b)   (c)   (d)

crystal with cleavage
N–S

crystal with cleavage
N–S

Figure 3.5   A biotite crystal viewed in plane-polarised light, exhibiting pleochroism: (a) with cleavage north–south (weakly coloured); (b) rotated through 90°, with cleavage east–west (strongly coloured); (c) rotated a further 90°, with cleavage north–south (weakly coloured); (d) rotated a further 90°, with cleavage east–west (strongly coloured).

3.2.4   Extinction positions

When two polarising filters are held up to the light and their permitted vibration directions are parallel, light is transmitted. If one of the filters is then rotated through 360°, there will be two positions (at 90° and 270°) when the vibration directions are at right angles to one another, and at which no light is transmitted. In these positions, the polarisers (often called polars) are thus said to be *crossed*. You will see this for yourself in Activity 3.2.

■   How would the intensity of any transmitted light change if an isotropic crystal was rotated between two crossed polars?

☐   No light would be transmitted, irrespective of the orientation of the crystal. Thus isotropic minerals always appear black when viewed between crossed polars.

If an anisotropic mineral is placed between the crossed polars, the result is quite different. On entering the crystal, the plane-polarised beam splits into two plane-polarised beams at right angles to each other, constrained to the permitted vibration directions of the crystal. When a permitted vibration direction is parallel to the plane of polarisation of the beam, however, the beam does not split and the polarised beam is transmitted in that same plane. On emerging, this beam is effectively blocked by the other (crossed) polariser. As this happens for both permitted directions of the crystal, and as each is parallel to the plane of polarisation twice in a full 360° revolution, four **extinction positions** at 90° to each other are observable when an anisotropic mineral is rotated between crossed polars.

These effects are summarised in Figure 3.6. In (a)–(d), white light enters the first polarising filter and is polarised in the east–west plane. In each case this plane coincides with one of the permitted vibration directions in the mineral (when in the east–west position). Light then passes through the mineral, still polarised in the east–west plane. However, it is polarised at right angles to the permitted vibration direction of the second polariser, which therefore prevents the light from passing. Darkness results and the mineral is in extinction.

Figure 3.6(e) illustrates what happens between extinction positions. Light that has passed through the first polarising filter is polarised in the east–west plane as before. On entering the mineral it splits into two rays, polarised at right angles by the anisotropic mineral. These two rays then enter the second polariser. Their planes of polarisation are at an angle to the permitted direction of the second polariser, which constrains the transmitted component of each ray to the north–south plane, and so light passes through. The *intensity* of the transmitted light varies gradually from zero at the positions of extinction to a maximum at each position halfway between the extinction positions.

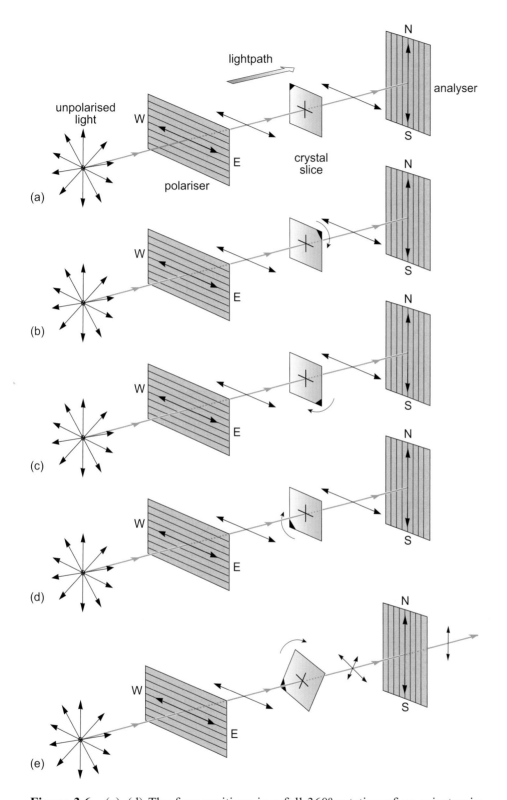

Figure 3.6 (a)–(d) The four positions in a full 360° rotation of an anisotropic mineral specimen, demonstrating extinction when a permitted vibration direction of the crystal is parallel to the plane of polarisation. (e) The general case when the two permitted directions of an anisotropic mineral do not coincide with the plane of polarisation.

3.2.5 Interference colours

As you have seen, in between extinction positions light is transmitted through crossed polars (Figure 3.6e), but in an anisotropic mineral the two light rays would travel at different speeds in each permitted vibration direction. The second, crossed polariser effectively combines the two rays, but as they have travelled at different speeds through the mineral, they arrive out of step, to an extent (called the optical path difference) that depends on the difference in refraction (the birefringence) and the thickness of the mineral (Figure 3.7). Consequently, the transmitted light is no longer the mixture of colours that makes white light, but is a single **interference colour** as a result of interference effects between the two waves when recombined. The theory associated with production of interference colours need not concern you here, but the consequences are important.

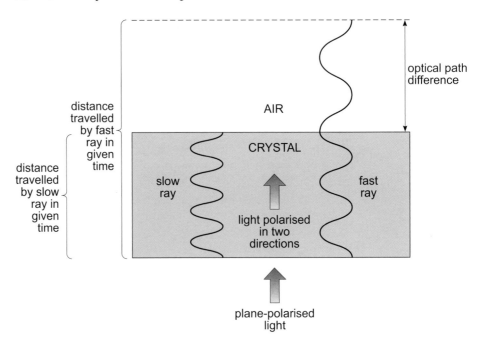

Figure 3.7 A light wave splits on entering a crystal through which the two rays travel at different speeds. The optical path difference produces interference colours.

The interference colour observed depends on the optical path difference and hence both the thickness of the mineral and the birefringence of the crystal in its particular orientation. A whole range of these interference colours can be seen when viewing a shallow wedge of quartz between crossed polars. Effectively, because the thickness of the wedge changes gradually while the birefringence remains the same throughout, the sequence of colours is a consequence of the transmitted rays becoming more and more out of step. The result is a 'spectrum' of interference colours called **Newton's scale of colours** – depicted on the **Michel–Levy chart** in Figure 3.8.

If the thickness of minerals to be observed were held constant, then the interference colours of the transmitted light would depend only on the difference in the refractive indices (the birefringence) for the light path in a

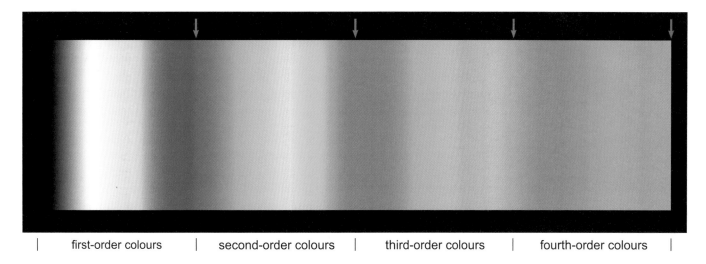

| first-order colours | second-order colours | third-order colours | fourth-order colours |

Figure 3.8 The Michel–Levy chart. Interference colours viewed through a quartz wedge, increasing in thickness from left to right, as viewed between crossed polars. The colours are divided into different orders (see text), separated by pinkish-purple bands, as indicated by the red arrows along the top.

given crystal. To see the more distinct interference colours shown in the left side of the chart (Figure 3.8), produced at the thin end of the wedge, the waves must not be too far out of step, so the mineral path must be short. In practice, slices of rock ground down to a thickness of just 30 μm ensure the transparency of most minerals, yet are sufficiently thick for distinct interference colours to be visible. By using this standard thickness of rock slices prepared for optical microscopy, uniformity is maintained, so that all observations of optical features are consistent from mineral to mineral and rock slice to rock slice.

The colour scale of the Michel–Levy chart can be divided into sections, called **orders**, separated by pinkish-purple bands (Figure 3.8). The more distinct colours at the thin end of the wedge are called low-order colours, and the lighter, less distinct colours at the thicker end are called high-order colours. For a slice of constant thickness, higher-order colours are produced by a mineral exhibiting higher birefringence. Calcite, with its high degree of anisotropy, is such a mineral.

When looking at interference colours, it is important to be aware of possible ambiguity in using the Michel–Levy chart. Some colours – particularly yellows and greens – appear in several places (i.e. in different orders) on the chart. Sometimes it can be difficult to establish the order of a particular interference colour. In general, higher-order colours appear much more washed out and pastel-like than lower-order colours, which are brighter and more vivid (Figure 3.8).

The refractive indices of an anisotropic mineral are related to its crystallographic axes and so its birefringence will vary according to its crystallographic orientation. This is an important point. If a single crystal of a mineral were taken and sliced in many different orientations, the interference colour would be different for each section – even for sections of the same thickness. In a rock that contains crystals of the same mineral in many different orientations, there will be differences in refractive index, hence birefringence, so that many different interference colours will be observed. However, the extent to which refractive indices can vary, and therefore the range of birefringence, is limited for any given mineral. In practice, it is the *greatest difference* in refractive index (i.e. the largest birefringence) and the **maximum interference colour** that can be identified, that is taken as characteristic (and can be diagnostic) of a particular mineral.

However, for some anisotropic minerals, slices can be cut in such a way that the refractive indices of the two plane-polarised rays are the same. This applies to minerals of the tetragonal, hexagonal and trigonal systems, when looking down their long (z) axes. Such a slice is often referred to as a **basal section**.

- ■ How would such a mineral, sliced perpendicular to its long axis, appear between crossed polars?

- ☐ It would be in darkness throughout when rotated, just like an isotropic mineral.

- ■ What would be the range of interference colours visible for such a mineral present as grains in random orientations?

- ☐ They would range from a maximum interference colour down through a range of intervening colours on the Michel–Levy chart to black.

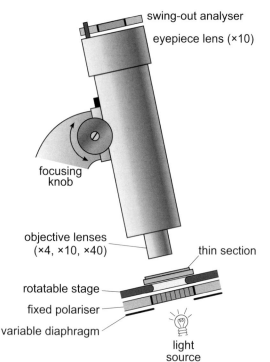

Figure 3.9 Schematic representation of the polarising microscope.

Labels: swing-out analyser; eyepiece lens (×10); focusing knob; objective lenses (×4, ×10, ×40); rotatable stage; fixed polariser; variable diaphragm; thin section; light source

Activity 3.2 Polarisation, extinction and interference colours

This activity involves using sheets of Polaroid and a gypsum slice to investigate extinction and interference effects.

3.3 Minerals and the polarising microscope

3.3.1 Introduction to the polarising microscope

The polarising microscope enables the examination of mineral grains and observation of the properties outlined in Section 3.2. A polarising microscope is very similar to an ordinary microscope except that it has two polarising filters and a rotating stage on which the sample is placed. Figure 3.9 illustrates a typical layout. Plane-polarised light is produced by passing white light through a polarising filter (the polariser) located beneath the rotating stage. The plane-polarised light then passes through the sample, which is presented as a thin slice of rock, 30 μm thick, mounted on a glass slide – this is a **thin section** (Figure 3.10). A magnified image is produced using two sets of lenses: a lower, **objective lens**, and an upper, **eyepiece lens**. The magnification can be varied by changing the objective lens. The image is focused by moving the lens assembly up or down, using the focusing knob. It is usual to start by looking at a thin section using plane-polarised light and low magnification. After this, the second polarising filter, the **analyser**, can be inserted to view the specimen between crossed polars.

In this course, the Virtual Microscope substitutes for the polarising microscope. You will have the opportunity to familiarise yourself with the features of the polarising microscope in Activity 3.3 and the functionality of the Virtual Microscope in Activity 3.4.

Activity 3.3 Introduction to the polarising microscope

This activity involves watching a short piece of video on DVD and an Interactive Screen Experiment (ISE) that introduces you to the features of a polarising microscope, and its use in the study of rocks and minerals.

Figure 3.10 A typical thin section (true size).

Activity 3.4 Introduction to the Virtual Microscope

This activity introduces you to the interface and functionality of the Virtual Microscope, which will enable you to investigate minerals and rocks as you would with a polarising microscope.

3.3.2 Minerals in thin section

Microscopic examination of a rock in thin section enables its constituent minerals and its textural properties to be identified. These are important and essential steps in establishing a rock's identity and in deducing how it was formed. The Virtual Microscope is designed to provide images as would be seen using a real polarising microscope. Views of numerous rock thin sections are available in plane-polarised light (PPL) and between crossed polars (XP), at different magnifications and at selected rotation points. The main optical properties used to identify minerals in both plane-polarised light and between crossed polars are outlined below.

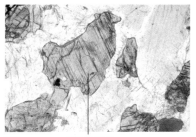

(a) pyroxene

In plane-polarised light

Relief. **Relief** is the term used to describe the degree to which edges and surface imperfections of crystals are visible in plane-polarised light. Minerals with a refractive index very different from that of the mounting glue are said to have high relief as they appear to 'stand out' from the slide (as for pyroxene in Figure 3.11a): grain boundaries are easily seen and surface imperfections appear pronounced. Minerals with refractive indices similar to that of the mounting glue are said to have low relief: individual grain boundaries are not easily observed and the minerals are featureless and almost invisible in plane-polarised light (as for plagioclase in Figure 3.11b). If the mineral is highly anisotropic (e.g. calcite), the relief may vary as the stage is rotated: the transmitted light sampling first one permitted vibration direction, then the other.

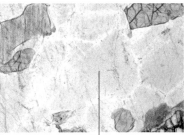

(b) plagioclase

Figure 3.11 (a) Pyroxene, a high-relief mineral that stands out – parallel cleavage traces are clearly visible. (b) Plagioclase, a featureless low-relief mineral.

Cleavage. **Cleavage traces** may be seen as sets of parallel straight lines cutting through a mineral section (Figure 3.11a). The presence, number and angular relationships of cleavage traces can be diagnostic for some minerals. Micas have one good strong cleavage (Figure 2.9c); pyroxenes and amphiboles have two cleavage planes, which intersect at about 90° and 120°, respectively, when basal sections are viewed in cross-section (Figure 4.2).

Colour and pleochroism. Many coloured silicate minerals are rich in iron (e.g. ferromagnesian minerals). If the colour changes as the mineral is rotated in plane-polarised light, the mineral is said to be pleochroic (i.e. the mineral absorbs light differently in different orientations – a concept met in Section 3.2.3). Biotite (dark mica) and amphiboles are good examples of pleochroic minerals, biotite commonly having characteristic pale- to dark-brown pleochroism (Figure 3.5).

Opaque minerals. Many opaque minerals are metal oxides, such as hematite (Fe_2O_3) and ilmenite ($FeTiO_3$), or sulfides, such as pyrite (FeS_2). Opaque minerals transmit no light – even in 30 μm thin sections: they appear black when viewed in both plane-polarised light and between crossed polars (in any orientation). Opaque minerals should not be confused with non-opaque minerals that are isotropic and appear black only between crossed polars.

Between crossed polars

Isotropic minerals. Isotropic minerals (e.g. garnet and fluorite) belong to the cubic system and, like glass, which is a disordered solid (Section 2.2), always appear black between crossed polars (e.g. the garnet in Figure 4.4c), regardless of their orientation but, unlike opaque minerals, will transmit light when viewed in plane-polarised light.

Anisotropic minerals. An anisotropic mineral (most minerals) will normally display an interference colour when viewed between crossed polars, and will pass in and out of extinction (at 90° intervals) as the stage is rotated. The interference colour depends on the crystallographic orientation of the mineral. When an anisotropic mineral is viewed in an orientation whereby the refractive indices in the permitted directions are the same (i.e. down the long axes of tetragonal, hexagonal and trigonal minerals), the mineral appears dark as the stage is rotated (i.e. it behaves like an isotropic mineral). This would be a basal section.

Interference colour. The Michel–Levy chart is used to estimate whether a mineral has high-order or low-order interference colours. When several grains of the same mineral are present, it is necessary to look for the one that shows the highest-order interference colour, which corresponds to the maximum birefringence.

Extinction. Cleavage traces can also be observed between crossed polars. Because cleavage planes are usually related to crystallographic axes, there is often a relationship between cleavage direction and the position at which the mineral goes into extinction. When cleavage traces are parallel or perpendicular to a mineral's permitted vibration directions, the extinction position is parallel to the cleavage and is referred to as **straight extinction**.

When the extinction position is at an angle to the cleavage trace, the mineral shows **inclined extinction**.

Twinning. A twinned crystal consists of regions that are structurally related to each other across a twin plane (Section 2.5). These regions are called twin components and, when viewed between crossed polars, adjacent components will go into extinction in different positions. Simple twins comprise just two components, side by side. However, some minerals (e.g. plagioclase feldspar), feature multiple twin components and, when viewed between crossed polars, have a striped appearance (Figure 4.18c). Rotating the crystal causes the bright and dark stripes to swap over.

Activity 3.5   Exploring mineral properties in thin section

In this activity, you will use the Virtual Microscope to investigate some of the properties exhibited by minerals in thin section.

The next chapter will focus on the recognition of the main rock-forming minerals using these properties. For ease of reference, the optical properties of these minerals are summarised on *Reference Card 1*. Although optical microscopy still has great value, providing an essential contextual framework for studying minerals and deducing how their characteristics and interrelationships reveal the manner of their formation, there are today many sophisticated procedures that can be used to extend our knowledge of minerals. A flavour of some of these is provided in Box 3.2.

Box 3.2   Determining mineral chemistry

Nowadays, interpreting the behaviour of rocks during their formation and subsequent events requires the chemical composition of their constituent minerals to be quantified. This can be done with modern instrumentation. In particular it can be important to determine the composition of individual grains, and even the variation within a grain. Appropriate modern microanalytical techniques use the electron microprobe (EMP), laser ablation inductively coupled plasma mass spectrometry (LA-ICP-MS) and the ion microprobe (IMP).

The electron microprobe technique involves directing a focused electron beam at a polished surface of a mineral grain. X-rays that are specific for each constituent element are emitted from the mineral. By measuring the intensity of the X-rays that characterise different elements, the major and minor element composition of 'spots' only a few μm across can be obtained. Alternatively, the beam may be scanned across the surface of mineral grains to produce X-ray maps of elemental concentrations. Another way of mapping minerals is by back-scattered electron (BSE) imaging. This is an image of the electrons that are scattered or bounced back by atoms bombarded by the electron beam. The number of electrons back-scattered is proportional to the mean atomic mass of the spot under the beam. So, brighter areas of the image represent minerals containing heavier elements (e.g. Fe and Ca) and darker areas represent minerals containing lighter elements (e.g. Si, Al, Mg and Na) (see Figure 3.12).

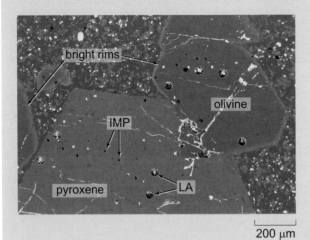

200 μm

Figure 3.12   Back-scattered electron image of minerals in a lava from the Solomon Islands. The large holes are due to laser ablation (LA), whereas the small holes are from ion microprobe analysis (IMP).

LA-ICP-MS uses a laser probe to melt a hole in a mineral; the vaporised (ablated) material is then analysed by mass spectrometer for its trace element, and sometimes its isotope, compositions. Spot sizes are 40–100 μm; which is generally larger than those of the EMP, but lower concentrations can be determined.

The ion microprobe uses an ion beam to remove (sputter) very small amounts of material from a spot 100 nm to 40 μm in size. The sputtered material is then analysed by mass spectrometer for its isotope and trace element compositions.

These micro-analytical techniques can be used to investigate the crystallisation history of an igneous rock. The back-scattered electron image in Figure 3.12 shows several large crystals of the minerals olivine and pyroxene surrounded by finer-grained crystals in a lava from the Solomon Islands in the western Pacific. EMP analysis reveals (Figure 3.13) that the bright rim around the edge of the olivine crystals is rich in iron, but the iron content decreases inwards until, from about 50 μm in from the rim, through the central part of the grain, the olivine has a constant (magnesium-rich) composition. This chemical profile is interpreted as being due to the diffusion of iron and magnesium between the surrounding magma and the olivine crystal just prior to eruption of the lava. The large pyroxene crystal also has a regular compositional variation around its edges, but this can be revealed only by LA-ICP-MS and IMP analysis of the trace element contents, which increase near the edge of the crystal.

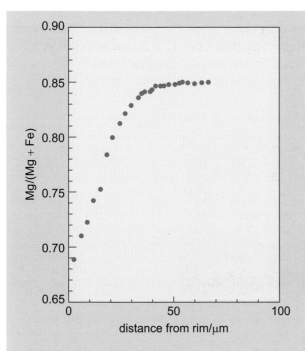

Figure 3.13 Element compositional traverse by EMP analysis of the olivine crystal shown in Figure 3.12.

If the temperature of the lava is known (by calculation from the chemistry of the lava and the minerals), it is possible to use the diffusion profile (the compositional gradient) in the rim to calculate how long the crystals had resided in the melt just prior to eruption. In this example, diffusion modelling reveals that the large crystals were there for 13.8 ± 1.4 days at a temperature of 1100 °C. This was long enough to produce the iron-rich rim of the olivine. The uniform internal compositions indicate that these crystals had originally crystallised elsewhere in the magmatic system.

3.4 Summary of Chapter 3

1 Light consists of electromagnetic waves that vibrate in all directions at 90° to the direction of travel of the light beam. White light is a mixture of coloured light with a range of frequencies.

2 The change in speed of light as it travels between media of different densities is known as refraction. The ratio of the speed of light in a given medium and its speed in air (strictly, in a vacuum) is the refractive index of that medium.

3 A polarising filter allows light to pass through, vibrating in one plane known as the permitted vibration direction. The light is plane-polarised.

4 Plane-polarised light passing through an anisotropic mineral splits into two plane-polarised rays that vibrate at 90° to each other. These rays travel at different speeds and give rise to double refraction, a property that is well developed in transparent calcite rhombs.

5   In plane-polarised light, some minerals absorb different wavelengths of light depending on the orientation of the crystal. This produces colours that vary with crystal orientation: a property known as pleochroism.

6   When an isotropic crystal (with the same optical properties in all directions) is placed between two polarising filters with their permitted vibration directions at 90° (i.e. crossed polars), no light will pass through, irrespective of the mineral's orientation (it appears uniformly black on rotation). Cubic minerals show this effect.

7   When an anisotropic crystal (with different optical properties in different crystallographic directions) is placed between two polarising filters and the mineral is rotated through 360°, there are four positions of darkness (extinction positions) that are 90° apart, between which the mineral appears coloured (has an interference colour) with an intensity that peaks halfway between extinction positions.

8   The difference in refractive index of light rays passing along the permitted vibration directions of an anisotropic mineral is its birefringence. When two such rays emerge, they are out of step, and when recombined on passing through a second, crossed polariser, interference colours are produced.

9   The sequence of interference colours as produced by increasing birefringence and simulated by a quartz wedge is represented on a Michel–Levy chart. Maximum interference colours can be diagnostic of particular minerals.

10 Opaque minerals do not transmit light of any kind.

11 A polarising microscope with a rotating stage and two polarising filters provides the facility to observe a range of diagnostic optical properties for mineral grains presented as a thin slice, 30 μm thick. Such rock slices mounted on glass are known as thin sections.

12 Other key diagnostic optical properties of minerals include relief, cleavage traces and twinning.

3.5   Objectives for Chapter 3

Now you have completed this chapter, you should be able to:

3.1 Suggest different ways in which light passing through a crystalline material is modified.

3.2 Define the terms refractive index and birefringence.

3.3 Explain the meaning of the terms isotropic and anisotropic, permitted vibration direction, double refraction and pleochroism.

3.4 Describe how plane-polarised light passes through an anisotropic crystal on the stage of a polarising microscope.

3.5 Explain the origin of interference colours in anisotropic materials.

3.6 Describe how to identify an unknown mineral (in thin section) using a polarising microscope.

Now try the following questions to test your understanding of Chapter 3.

Question 3.1

A slice of an unknown mineral has been examined with a polarising microscope. In plane-polarised light the mineral appeared colourless, but when viewed between crossed polars it appeared dark, and remained dark as the mineral was rotated. To what crystal system is this mineral likely to belong?

Question 3.2

In plane-polarised light, a thin section of a mineral shows very high relief, but as the stage is rotated through 90°, this changes to very low relief. Why does the relief change with orientation? What prediction can you make about the interference colour for this mineral?

Question 3.3

In Chapter 2, you were introduced to the crystal structures of two polymorphs of carbon: diamond and graphite. Based on your knowledge of these structures, what prediction(s) can you make about the optical properties of diamond and graphite?

Chapter 4   Rock-forming minerals

4.1   Introduction

Over 90 chemical elements occur naturally on Earth. You might expect them to combine in ways that would form an almost infinite number of minerals. In fact, the total number of minerals discovered is only about 4000, and the number of commonly occurring *rock-forming* minerals is very much smaller. One reason for so few common minerals is that most elements have low abundances and rarely occur in sufficient quantities to combine and form minerals. Thus the more widely occurring rock-forming minerals represent combinations of a small number of readily available ingredients, those elements which are more abundant in the Earth's crust and mantle, as listed in Table 4.1.

Table 4.1   The average composition of the Earth's crust and mantle (only the more abundant elements are listed).

Element	Symbol	% in crust (by mass)	% in mantle (by mass)
oxygen	O	46.6	44.6
silicon	Si	27.7	21.4
aluminium	Al	8.3	2.2
iron	Fe	5.0	5.9
calcium	Ca	3.6	2.3
sodium	Na	2.8	0.2
potassium	K	2.6	trace
magnesium	Mg	2.1	22.7
others		1.3	0.7
total		100.0	100.0

From Table 4.1, it is clear that oxygen and silicon are by far the most abundant elements in the crust and mantle. Minerals containing silicon combined with oxygen are called **silicate minerals**, and are the single most important mineral group – making up over 90% of the Earth's crust and almost all of the mantle.

The non-silicate minerals (of which calcite is perhaps the most familiar example) contain other chemical groups, such as carbon combined with oxygen (**carbonates**) and metals combined with oxygen (**oxides**) or sulfur (**sulfides**).

The following sections contain descriptions of the crystal structures of important rock-forming minerals. *Note*: you are not expected to remember specific details of the structures, merely the essential attributes of, and differences between, the structures of the main mineral groups.

The properties of the rock-forming minerals are summarised on *Reference Card 1*. Using this as a reference, you should be able to distinguish between the major rock-forming minerals on the basis of their physical properties. You are not expected to memorise them all, but to become familiar with the more diagnostic properties.

4.2 Silicate mineral structures

Silicate minerals all share the same basic building block: a silicon atom bonded to four oxygen atoms at the corners of a tetrahedron, called the **silicate group** (or SiO_4 group) (Figure 4.1).

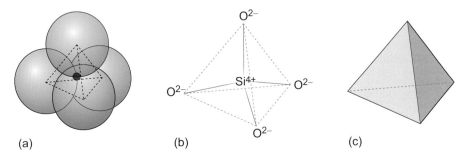

(a)   (b)   (c)

Figure 4.1 (a) The SiO_4 tetrahedral unit with atoms of oxygen (red) and silicon (grey) shown at true relative scale. (b) The atomic structure of the SiO_4 unit, showing how the silicon and oxygen atoms are linked. (c) The simplified SiO_4 tetrahedron, the basic shape of the SiO_4 unit.

The wide range of silicate minerals that exists in nature owes much to a property of the SiO_4 group, known as **polymerisation**. Polymerisation generally leads to increasingly complex mineral structures. At the simplest level, SiO_4 groups bond with metal cations, forming **isolated groups** (Figure 4.2) as in olivine minerals (Section 4.3.1). With increasing polymerisation, the SiO_4 group can also build two- and three-dimensional structures, such as chains, sheets and frameworks, by linking up SiO_4 tetrahedra. With the exception of the silica minerals, where all the oxygens are shared, these structures are also linked by a variety of cations to make more complex three-dimensional structures.

The first stage of polymerisation of SiO_4 groups involves the formation of **chain structures**, as in pyroxene minerals (Section 4.4.1), produced by corner-sharing of the oxygen atoms (Figure 4.2). The ratio of silicon to oxygen atoms increases from 1 : 4 in structures with isolated SiO_4 groups, to 1 : 3 in chain structures. The degree of polymerisation increases further in more complex chains (Figure 4.2), as in amphibole minerals (Section 4.4.2), and the ratio of silicon to oxygen increases to 4 : 11. Further polymerisation produces **sheet structures**, whereby tetrahedra are linked in two dimensions to form sheets (Figure 4.2). These sheets are bonded together by a variety of chemical groups, such as hydroxyl (OH^-) or metal cations, to form sandwich structures and the Si : O ratio rises to 2 : 5. In fully polymerised three-dimensional **framework structures**, as in quartz (Section 4.6.1), the Si : O ratio reaches 1 : 2.

Structural form	Arrangement of tetrahedra	T : O	Mineral examples	Additional comments
isolated groups	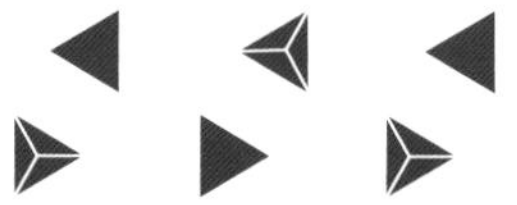	1 : 4	olivine, e.g. Mg_2SiO_4 garnet, e.g. $Mg_3Al_2(SiO_4)_3$	Dense compact structures. Crystals have equidimensional shapes and no cleavage.
single 1D chain structures	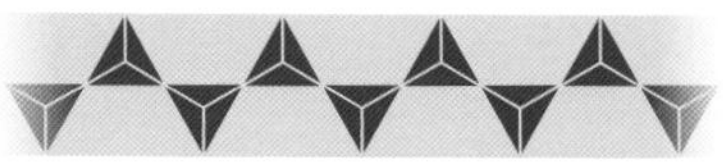	1 : 3	pyroxene, e.g. $Mg_2Si_2O_6$	Pyroxenes are generally prismatic and dense. They have two well-developed cleavages at nearly 90°. 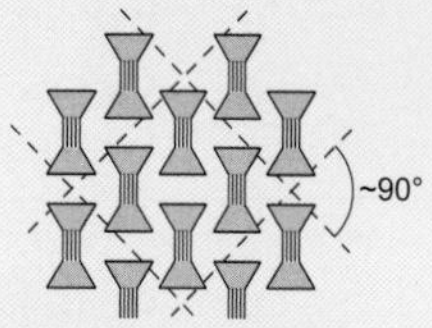 chains viewed end-on; cleavage develops where bonding between chains is weakest 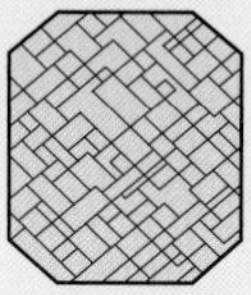 — typical near-90° cleavage pattern in pyroxene viewed end-on to chains
double 1D chain structures		4 : 11	amphibole, e.g. $Ca_2Mg_5(Si_8O_{22})(OH)_2$	Amphiboles are similarly shaped but less compact and less dense than pyroxenes because holes in the double chains accommodate $(OH)^-$ groups. They have two well-developed cleavages at nearly 60°/120°. 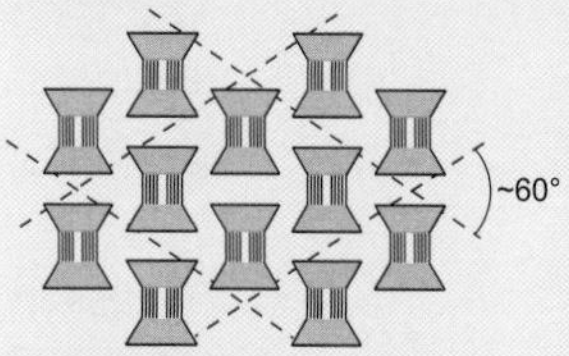 double chains viewed end-on; cleavage develops where bonding between double chains is weakest 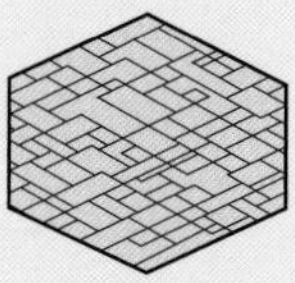 — typical near-60°/120° cleavage pattern in amphibole viewed end-on to double chains
2D sheet structures	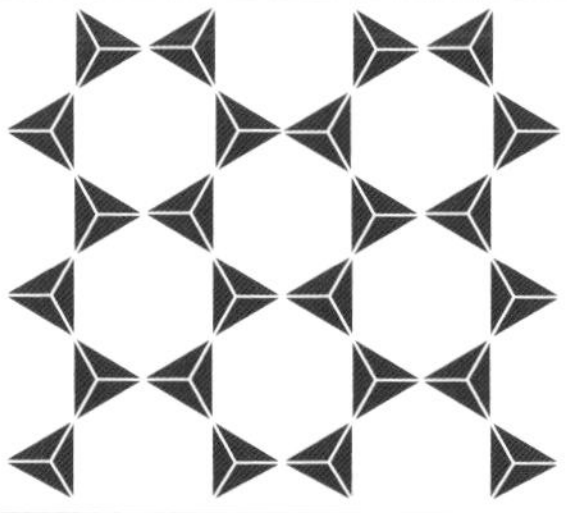	2 : 5	mica, e.g. $KMg_3(AlSi_3O_{10})(OH)_2$ clay minerals	Sheet silicates are tabular minerals with open structures and low densities. The open spaces in the sheets accommodate $(OH)^-$ groups. Although the sheets themselves are strong, there is a very well-defined cleavage between them where the bonding is weak.
3D frameworks		1 : 2	quartz, SiO_2 feldspar, e.g. $NaAlSi_3O_8$	Quartz has a rigid framework with strong Si—O bonds only. Feldspars have some weaker bonds (between alkali metal atoms and oxygen) and show two cleavages at nearly 90°. With no $(OH)^-$ groups, these structures are more compact than micas.

Figure 4.2 Structural classification of common silicate minerals, based on polymerisation of the silicate tetrahedron. The ratio of the tetrahedral (T) sites to oxygen (O) sites increases with polymerisation as more oxygen atoms are shared between tetrahedral sites. The structures shown are only very small parts of what are effectively infinite structures. The right-hand column of the diagram illustrates how the atomic structures affect mineral properties.

In some minerals, aluminium replaces silicon in some of the SiO_4 tetrahedra producing AlO_4 groups. It is therefore more appropriate to think of oxygen atoms being shared between tetrahedral (T) sites, which may contain either silicon or aluminium. So, more generally, increasing polymerisation results in an increase in the ratio of tetrahedral sites to oxygen – the T : O ratio (Figure 4.2). The net charge on the SiO_4 group is −4, but on the AlO_4 group it is −5, so additional positive charges are required to compensate for the excess negative charge on the tetrahedral groups. These may be provided by cations, commonly metals, residing in cavities or interstices in the tetrahedral structure (Section 2.4.2). Figure 4.2 summarises the structural styles of the major silicate mineral groups. In the following sections, you will look at each of these groups in more detail.

4.3   Minerals with isolated SiO_4 tetrahedra

Minerals with isolated SiO_4 tetrahedra have the simplest structures. They also have the lowest T : O ratio (i.e. 1 : 4).

4.3.1   Olivine

The name 'olivine' refers to a group of minerals with a continuous spread of chemical compositions between **forsterite** (Mg_2SiO_4) and **fayalite** (Fe_2SiO_4), and the formula is written as $(Mg,Fe)_2SiO_4$, indicating that atoms (in fact, ions) of magnesium and iron can substitute for each other. This kind of chemical mixture is called a **solid solution** and involves ions having similar *sizes* and similar *charges* (e.g. Mg^{2+} and Fe^{2+}). For a complete solid solution, as developed between forsterite and fayalite, the substituting ions must have similar **ionic radii** (a measure of their size), so that either ion can fit into the same interstitial site in the crystal structure.

Olivine is an important example of a structure with isolated tetrahedra. Every SiO_4 group has a net charge of −4 (Figure 4.1b), and because the crystal has to be electrically neutral, olivine contains two doubly charged (2+) cations per SiO_4 unit. Silicon atoms reside in tetrahedral interstices (i.e. at the centres of SiO_4 tetrahedra), whereas octahedral interstices contain the larger magnesium and iron atoms (Section 2.4.2). These are close-packed, largely ionic structures, which explains why, compared with other silicates, olivine has a relatively high density. The structure is also strong in three dimensions, making olivine a hard mineral, without any good cleavage. Olivine has a characteristic olive-green colour (Figure 4.3a) that becomes darker with increasing iron content.

Olivine is stable at high temperatures and pressures, and forms about 60% of the Earth's upper mantle. It crystallises at high temperatures from magmas rich in iron and magnesium and relatively poor in silica (SiO_2). In such rocks, where olivine is one of the first minerals to crystallise as the magma cools, it may develop well-formed crystals, surrounded by later-crystallising minerals (which tend to be smaller, and lack such ideal crystal shapes).

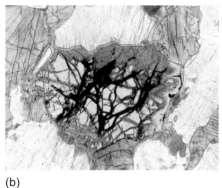

(a) (b) (c)

Figure 4.3 (a) Olivine 'pebbles' with distinctive olive-green colour (dish is 3 cm across). (b) Plane-polarised light image of olivine in a gabbro. The many irregular cracks containing iron oxide (optically opaque) are characteristic of olivine, as is an absence of cleavage. This olivine has partially altered to a green- or brown-coloured mineral, in this case, serpentine. Where the olivine is not altered, it is normally colourless and exhibits no pleochroism (field of view 2.6 mm across). (c) The same field of view as in (b) between crossed polars, the olivine having characteristic second-order interference colours.

Olivine is prone to alteration at lower temperatures under hydrous conditions, especially during weathering. Under the microscope, evidence of this alteration in olivine crystals takes the form of new minerals, such as greenish or brownish **serpentine**, and curved, irregular cracks filled with iron oxide (opaque) (Figure 4.3b and c).

Activity 4.1 Olivine in hand specimen and thin section

This activity will help you to recognise olivine in hand specimen and in thin section.

4.3.2 Garnet

Like olivine, the **garnet** group of minerals is also based on a structure of isolated SiO_4 tetrahedra and, as a result, garnets are also dense minerals and are commonly formed at high pressures both in the Earth's crust and mantle. Garnets are found in many crustal metamorphic rocks, especially those formed at depths greater than ~24 km, and are ubiquitous in the upper mantle at depths greater than 85 km. Garnets may also occur in some igneous rocks.

Although the garnet crystal structure is complex, it belongs to the cubic system, so garnets are optically isotropic (Figure 4.4c). Garnets have the general chemical formula $A_3B_2(SiO_4)_3$ where A represents divalent (2+) metal ions and B represents trivalent (3+) metal ions. However, garnets have a wide range of chemical compositions; they may contain various combinations from aluminium, calcium, iron, magnesium or even rare-earth elements, such as yttrium.

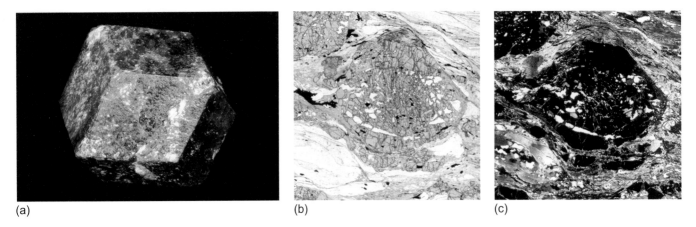

Figure 4.4 (a) Garnet in its distinctive dodecahedral (12-sided) form (MS X), due to its cubic crystal structure (long diagonal of the crystal face is 3.4 cm across). (b) Plane-polarised light image of a garnet in garnet mica schist. Garnet is a high-relief mineral that can be faintly coloured, depending on its composition (field of view 5.5 mm across). (c) The same field of view as in (b) between crossed polars; garnet is isotropic so stays black when the thin section is rotated. The grey and transparent streaks and spots in the garnet are quartz crystals included in the garnet as it grew.

Activity 4.2 Garnet in hand specimen and thin section

This activity will help you to recognise garnet in hand specimen and thin section.

4.4 Chain silicates

4.4.1 Pyroxene

The **pyroxene** group of minerals has the general formula $ABSi_2O_6$ (where A and B refer to divalent metal ions in the A and B sites, respectively). Some pyroxenes belong to the monoclinic system; others to the orthorhombic system. Important **clinopyroxenes** (monoclinic) include augite $(Ca(Mg,Fe)Si_2O_6)$, and **orthopyroxenes** (orthorhombic) include enstatite $(Mg_2Si_2O_6)$.

■ Which metal atoms occupy which sites in augite?

☐ Using the general formula $ABSi_2O_6$, Ca occupies the A site, and the B site contains a mixture of Mg and Fe atoms. Note that the formula of augite implies that there is solid solution from $CaMgSi_2O_6$ to $CaFeSi_2O_6$.

All pyroxenes are formed of single chains of SiO_4 tetrahedra, similar to that depicted in Figure 4.2. In three dimensions, the chains are interconnected via strong bonds to cations at the B site. The chains that are bonded by the B-site cations are then stacked together to form a strong structure. Adjacent chains mesh into each other and are weakly bonded by a second set of cations, residing in A sites, so for every two SiO_3 chain units, there is one A site and one B site.

The differences between the *A* and *B* sites are important and are key to understanding the mechanical properties of pyroxene. The pyroxene structure is not uniformly strong and the regions between the chains are relatively weak such that they are likely to break – or cleave – along these directions. This gives two good cleavage directions at approximately 90° (strictly 87° (or 93°)) to each other (Figure 4.2).

■   When you observe pyroxene cleavages in thin section, will the traces always be at about 90° to each other?

☐   The two sets of cleavage traces will only be at about 90° to each other if you are looking down the length of the crystal. This is the basal section for pyroxene. If you were looking perpendicular to this direction (i.e. sideways onto the length of the crystal), there would appear to be only one set of parallel cleavage traces. This is true of the crystal illustrated in Figure 4.5b. Note, however, that if you were looking *obliquely* to the basal section the cleavage traces would form a diamond-shaped outline.

In pyroxenes where one set of cleavage traces is visible in thin section (Figure 4.5b), it is easy to distinguish orthopyroxenes, with straight extinction, from clinopyroxenes, with inclined extinction.

(a)

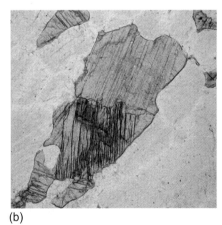
(b)

(c)

Figure 4.5 (a) A pyroxene in stubby prismatic form. (b) Plane-polarised light image of a clinopyroxene in a gabbro. Pyroxenes sometimes have a faint pleochroism. A single set of cleavage traces can be seen. (c) The same field of view as in (b) between crossed polars, showing pyroxene with second-order interference colours.

Pyroxenes are important rock-forming minerals commonly found in many igneous and metamorphic rocks. Pyroxenes in basaltic igneous rocks have different compositions from those in andesites. Their occurrence is more restricted in metamorphic rocks but they can be important in those formed at high temperatures.

4.4.2 Amphibole

The **amphibole** group of minerals is chemically more complex than the pyroxenes. The general formula can be written as $AB_2C_5Si_8O_{22}(OH)_2$, where *A* represents a large cation such as Na, and *B* and *C* represent smaller cations, such as Ca or Mg. Amphiboles also contain the **hydroxyl group**, (OH), and are therefore **hydrous minerals**, in contrast to pyroxenes, which are **anhydrous minerals**.

Amphibole minerals contain double silicate chains (Figure 4.2) resembling the pyroxene structure, and likewise have two distinct cleavages. However, because these chains are wider than the pyroxene single chains, the cleavages intersect at about 60° or 120° (strictly 56° (or 124°)), as illustrated in Figures 4.2 and 4.6b.

One way to distinguish amphibole from pyroxene in thin section is by its roughly 60° (or 120°) cleavage in basal sections (Figure 4.6). Most often the cleavage is parallel and amphiboles have inclined extinction. Some common varieties are strongly pleochroic (some with yellowish-green turning to brown colours; some are deep blue turning to colourless).

Amphiboles are found in many metamorphic rocks and crystallise from hydrous magmas (containing water) that have moderate to high SiO_2 and Na_2O contents, such as andesites.

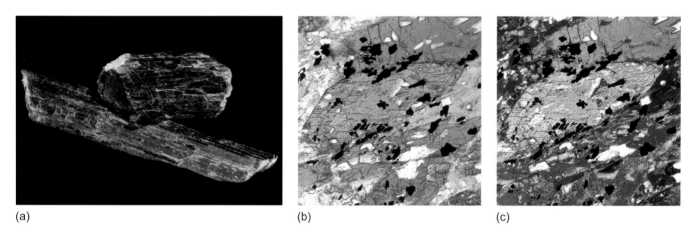

(a)   (b)   (c)

Figure 4.6 (a) An amphibole with a prismatic crystal form (shorter crystal is 3 cm long). (b) A plane-polarised light image of an amphibole in a metamorphic rock called amphibolite. This shows a basal section in which two cleavage planes intersect at about 120°. This amphibole has a strong pale greyish-green turning to dark greyish-green pleochroism (field of view 2 mm across). (c) The same field of view as in (b) between crossed polars. Although the amphibole has second-order interference colours, they can be masked by the strong body colour of the mineral – i.e. its colour in plane-polarised light.

Activity 4.3   Pyroxene and amphibole in hand specimen and thin section

This activity focuses on the features by which pyroxene and amphibole can be distinguished in hand specimen and thin section.

4.5   Sheet silicate minerals

The sheet silicates comprise a large number of different minerals, including micas. They all share the same basic building blocks: a tetrahedral sheet (Figure 4.7a), and one of two kinds of octahedral sheet.

The octahedral sheets can be thought of as layers of metal hydroxides. One kind of octahedral sheet is effectively a layer of magnesium hydroxide, $Mg(OH)_2$, where each magnesium atom is bonded to six OH groups at the corners of an octahedron. The octahedra are arranged in a plane, sharing edges, to form a *tri*octahedral sheet as each oxygen atom is shared between *three* octahedra (Figure 4.7b).

The other kind of octahedral sheet contains aluminium instead of magnesium, and is effectively a layer of aluminium hydroxide, $Al(OH)_3$. In this case each oxygen atom is shared between *two* octahedra, hence this is a *di*octahedral sheet (Figure 4.7c), and it leaves distinct holes in the structure. In sheet silicates, the sheets are combined to form composite structures: for example an octahedral sheet sandwiched between two tetrahedral sheets as shown in Figure 4.7d, and more schematically in Figure 4.7e.

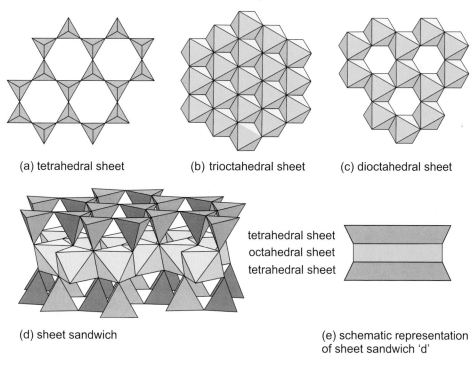

(a) tetrahedral sheet   (b) trioctahedral sheet   (c) dioctahedral sheet

(d) sheet sandwich

tetrahedral sheet
octahedral sheet
tetrahedral sheet

(e) schematic representation of sheet sandwich 'd'

Figure 4.7   Building blocks of sheet silicate minerals. (a) Part of a sheet made up of SiO_4 tetrahedra. (b) Part of a $Mg(OH)_2$ *tri*octahedral sheet, where every oxygen atom is shared between *three* octahedra. (c) Part of an $Al(OH)_3$ *di*octahedral sheet, where every oxygen atom is shared between *two* octahedra. (d) An oblique view of a sheet sandwich, formed by two tetrahedral sheets bonded to an octahedral sheet. (e) A schematic representation of the sheet sandwich in (d).

A property common to all sheet silicate minerals is their tendency to be soft, with near-perfect cleavage parallel to the sheets. They form distinctive, platy or flake-like crystals. With (OH) groups as part of their structure, they are all hydrous minerals.

4.5.1   The mica group

Mica is a general name given to a range of sheet silicate minerals that are commonly found in igneous, metamorphic and sedimentary rocks. In igneous rocks, they crystallise from hydrous magmas with medium to high silica contents; in metamorphic rocks the parallel alignment of mica crystals defines the foliation found in slates and schists (Chapter 8).

Micas have sandwich structures, weakly bonded by interlayer ions. Each sandwich contains a tetrahedral sheet on each side of an octahedral sheet (Figure 4.7d). Commonly one in four of the tetrahedra contains Al instead of Si (although the number of oxygen atoms remains unchanged), with the result that sheets have an excess negative charge. This is balanced by the presence of interlayer cations, such as K^+, between the sandwiches (Figure 4.8a).

The bonding inside a sandwich is very strong, but between sandwiches it is very weak (due to the interlayer ions), permitting one sandwich to slide past another. Thus, mica has one perfect cleavage, parallel to the layers, so it is easy to split a mica crystal into very thin flakes (see Digital Kit and MS II).

You have seen that there are two options for making the octahedral layers: either an $Al(OH)_3$ dioctahedral layer (Figure 4.7c), or a $Mg(OH)_2$ trioctahedral layer (Figure 4.7b). These give rise to two important mica minerals: **muscovite** ('white' mica; Figure 4.10a), which contains dioctahedral layers, and **biotite** ('dark' mica; Figure 4.9a), which contains trioctahedral layers in which Fe^{2+} commonly substitutes for Mg^{2+}.

■   Why should biotite commonly be dark and muscovite be white?

☐   Silicate minerals containing large amounts of Fe tend to have dark colours, and this is also true of biotite, which is often Fe rich. Muscovite contains little if any Fe, and so is usually pale coloured.

The structures of muscovite and biotite are given, in schematic form, in Figure 4.8a.

Micas are striking minerals under the microscope; biotites are often strongly coloured, and muscovites are colourless in plane-polarised light, but both have a perfect cleavage and vivid second- to third-order interference colours. The difference in colour between biotite, with strong pleochroism, and muscovite is diagnostic in thin section (Figures 4.9b and c; 4.10b and c). Note that basal sections show neither cleavage nor pleochroism.

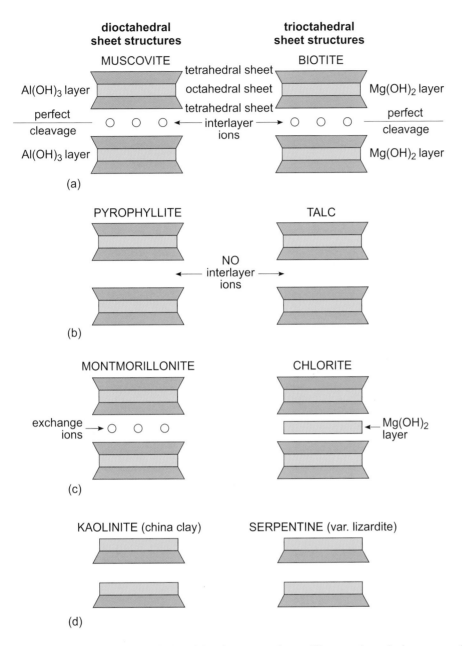

Figure 4.8 Structural relationships between sheet silicate minerals in terms of the stacking of tetrahedral and octahedral layers. On the left are minerals with dioctahedral layers; on the right are minerals with trioctahedral layers.

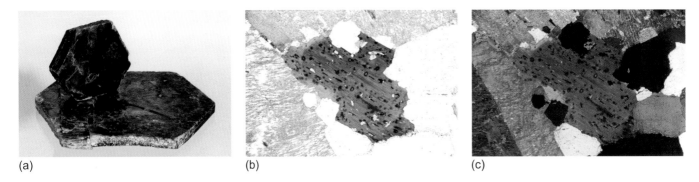

(a) (b) (c)

Figure 4.9 (a) Biotite, showing its strong basal cleavage (larger crystal is 7.5 cm across). (b) Plane-polarised light image of biotite in granite. The biotite displays strong brown pleochroism. The cleavage traces are also obvious and run NW–SE along the length of the grain. Dark circles in the biotite surround small grains of the mineral zircon, which contains small amounts of radioactive uranium. The dark circles are called pleochroic haloes and are due to radiation damage in the mineral structure (field of view 5.5 mm across). (c) The same field of view as in (b) between crossed polars; although biotite has second-order interference colours, they are masked by its strong body colour.

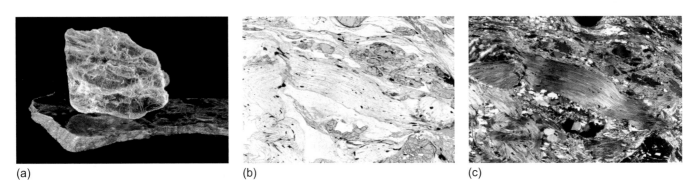

(a) (b) (c)

Figure 4.10 (a) Muscovite, showing its strong basal cleavage (smaller flake is 3 cm across). (b) Plane-polarised light image of muscovite in a garnet mica schist. The muscovite is colourless. Obvious cleavage traces run along the length of the grain, but because the rock is deformed, they have a bent or wavy appearance (field of view 7.5 mm across). (c) The same field of view as in (b) between crossed polars; muscovite has bright second- to third-order interference colours.

4.5.2 Clay minerals

Clay minerals are stable at low temperatures and tend to form from the chemical breakdown of medium- to high-temperature aluminium-rich silicate minerals in the presence of water. Various clay minerals are produced by chemical weathering of different minerals and are commonly found in fine-grained sediments, such as mudstones and siltstones. For example, the china clay (kaolinite) of Devon and Cornwall is derived from the decomposition of K-feldspar ($KAlSi_3O_8$) in granite. Montmorillonite is formed from the breakdown of volcanic ashes. Kaolinite and montmorillonite are related to the muscovite structure, with aluminium in dioctahedral layers (Figure 4.8), but there is no aluminium in the tetrahedral layers. Some clay minerals (such as montmorillonite) allow water molecules to reside between their sandwich layers, which gives the clay its plasticity as the layers slide over one another.

The structure of clay minerals enables them to have a wide range of industrial and domestic applications. The large gaps between the sheets, and the large areas of the sheets, mean that many clay minerals on a fine scale readily *ad*sorb ions and molecules onto crystal surfaces. The consequent *ab*sorbency in bulk of montmorillonite is important for its use as cat litter, and vermiculite (another clay mineral) may be used to retain moisture during seed germination. The platy structure of clays is beneficial for use in drilling muds that lubricate drill bits during drilling for crude oil.

Clays are very fine grained, so it is difficult to observe their optical properties, even with a polarising microscope.

4.5.3 Other sheet silicates

Some other sheet silicates that you are likely to meet include talc, chlorite and serpentine. These minerals have structures related to biotite, with magnesium (and iron) in trioctahedral layers (as summarised in the right-hand column of Figure 4.8). Unlike biotite, however, their tetrahedral layers contain no aluminium, only silicon. These layers, therefore, have no net electrical charge, and so no interlayer ions are required to balance charges. Without the interlayer ions, there is little to hold the layers together.

■ How would you expect the hardness of talc to compare with that of biotite?

☐ Without interlayer ions between the sandwich layers, minerals such as talc are much softer than biotite. Talc is one of the softest minerals known, with a hardness of 1 on Mohs' scale (Table 2.2).

All of these minerals are stable at low temperatures (and up to surprisingly high pressures) and tend to form (serpentine, especially) by the breakdown of high-temperature Mg-rich minerals, such as olivine (Mg_2SiO_4), under hydrous conditions. These minerals, therefore, contain hydroxyl groups and are common (serpentine and talc, especially) in basaltic and mantle rocks that have been altered by watery fluids. Chlorite is common in many low-temperature metamorphic rocks derived from sediments and from basaltic igneous rocks.

Pyrophyllite, with dioctahedral layers (Figure 4.8b), is a low-temperature metamorphic mineral found in aluminium-rich sedimentary rocks such as slates.

Activity 4.4 Micas in hand specimen and thin section

This activity will help you to recognise muscovite and biotite micas in hand specimen and thin section.

4.6 Framework silicates

Framework silicates are the most abundant silicates in the Earth's crust. They have complex crystal structures, with each SiO_4 tetrahedron joined to four others, producing a three-dimensional framework. In feldspars, some of the silicon atoms are replaced by aluminium, and singly charged cations (e.g. Na^+ or K^+) are required to maintain charge balance.

4.6.1 Silica minerals

The **silica minerals** have fully polymerised structures and are essentially pure silica. There are several minerals with the chemical formula SiO_2, although most of them are usually referred to as quartz, as it is difficult to recognise the differences between them in both hand specimen and thin section. The SiO_2 phase diagram (Figure 4.11) illustrates that at least five forms of SiO_2 can be found in the Earth's crust and a further high-pressure form called stishovite is stable at pressures greater than 7.5 GPa. At progressively higher pressures, the Si and O atoms are packed closer together so that coesite is denser than α-quartz and stishovite is denser than coesite. Silica minerals are very common in sedimentary, igneous and metamorphic rocks because they are chemically and mechanically stable under a wide range of conditions. Figure 4.11 can be used to predict which forms of SiO_2 are found in different rocks: α-quartz is found in sedimentary rocks whereas β-quartz is found in high-temperature/low-pressure metamorphic rocks. Coesite is a characteristic mineral of some high-pressure metamorphic rocks whereas stishovite has only ever been discovered in nature in meteorite impact sites where very high pressures and temperatures were developed. In igneous rocks, tridymite and cristobalite are restricted to lavas that crystallised rapidly from high-temperature silica-rich magmas.

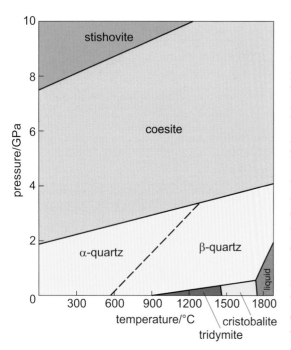

Figure 4.11 Phase diagram for SiO_2. The pascal is the SI unit of pressure (1 GPa = 10^9 Pa = 10^9 N m^{-2}.)

Question 4.1

What pressure would be required to convert silica into stishovite at 300 °C?

The strong, three-dimensional bonding in quartz, which is dominantly covalent on account of there being no metal cations present, means that there are no definite planes of weakness and, therefore, no cleavage. So, when broken, quartz shatters to form glassy fragments with a curved, conchoidal fracture (MS III). The strong bonding also makes quartz very hard and extremely resistant to chemical attack. Consequently, quartz grains can survive transport by wind or water over vast distances, eventually being deposited as sand grains.

Although quartz is very pure SiO_2, it can sometimes contain small amounts of impurities such as aluminium, iron, lithium and titanium. The effect of these impurities is to produce quite dramatic colours in what would otherwise be an entirely colourless mineral (Figures 2.6 and 4.12a).

Under the microscope, quartz lacks cleavage and colour and has low first-order, grey–white interference colours (Figure 4.12b and c). Being chemically stable, quartz crystals look clean compared with feldspars, which are almost always turbid or cloudy.

(a)

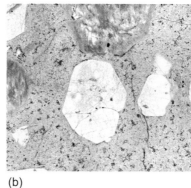
(b)

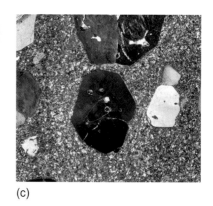
(c)

Figure 4.12 (a) A well-formed prismatic crystal of quartz (longest crystal length is 6 cm). (b) Plane-polarised light image of a quartz crystal in a silica-rich lava. The quartz is the well-formed crystal with low relief and no pleochroism in the centre of the image (field of view 7.5 mm across). (c) The same field of view as in (b) between crossed polars. Quartz has distinctive first-order grey interference colours and, when deformed (or strained) slightly, exhibits characteristic undulose (wavy) extinction, whereby not all of the crystal goes into extinction at the same time.

Activity 4.5   Quartz in hand specimen and thin section

This activity will help you to recognise quartz in hand specimen and thin section.

4.6.2   Feldspars

Feldspars are especially common minerals and make up about 60% of the Earth's crust. They crystallise from a wide spectrum of magmas and are found in many metamorphic and sedimentary rocks. The name feldspar refers to a *group* of silicate minerals that share the same basic structure. The three most important feldspar minerals are **orthoclase** ($KAlSi_3O_8$), **albite** ($NaAlSi_3O_8$) and **anorthite** ($CaAl_2Si_2O_8$).

At high temperatures there is complete solid solution between orthoclase and albite, as K and Na substitute for each other (in the same way that Fe and Mg substitute for each other in olivine). Feldspars with compositions within this range are called **alkali feldspars**. At lower temperatures the alkali feldspar solid solution is not complete, and if an alkali feldspar crystal of an intermediate composition (e.g. $Na_{0.3}K_{0.7}AlSi_3O_8$) were cooled very slowly, it would 'unmix' into Na-rich and K-rich phases – a process known as **exsolution** (meaning 'from solution'). The result is a crystal mainly of one composition (K-rich), containing streaks of another composition (Na-rich), producing what is known as **perthitic texture** (particularly noticeable in thin section when viewed between crossed polars). You will see examples of perthitic texture in Figure 4.13 and Activity 4.7.

There is also complete solid solution between albite and anorthite at high and intermediate temperatures: these are the **plagioclase feldspars**. Plagioclase feldspars crystallise from a range of magma compositions, depending on the

Figure 4.13 A twinned K-feldspar crystal that displays perthitic texture when viewed between crossed polars (field of view 3.25 mm across). The streaks of light-grey mineral have been exsolved.

proportion of Ca and Na available. Solid solution in plagioclase feldspars is rather more complex than in alkali feldspars, because Na^+ and Ca^{2+} have different charges. A **coupled substitution** is required to maintain charge balance whereby two substitutions occur simultaneously:

Na^+ substitutes for Ca^{2+} *and* Si^{4+} substitutes for Al^{3+}

This coupled substitution is more usually written as:

$$Na^+ + Si^{4+} \rightleftharpoons Ca^{2+} + Al^{3+}$$

There is no solid solution between $KAlSi_3O_8$ and $CaAl_2Si_2O_8$ because of the large size difference between K^+ and Ca^{2+} (about 30%). Ionic substitution is, therefore, not possible.

The overall compositional range of feldspars can be shown on a **ternary diagram** (Figure 4.14). Ternary diagrams are very useful tools in geology, and you will meet them again later in the course. Their use is explained in Box 4.1.

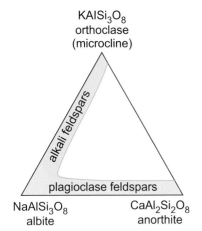

$KAlSi_3O_8$
orthoclase
(microcline)

alkali feldspars

plagioclase feldspars

$NaAlSi_3O_8$
albite

$CaAl_2Si_2O_8$
anorthite

Figure 4.14 A ternary diagram showing the extent of solid solution in alkali and plagioclase feldspar at high temperatures.

Box 4.1 Ternary diagrams

A ternary diagram can be used to plot the composition of a mineral (or indeed, any multi-component substance or mixture) in terms of three end-member components (A, B and C). The diagram consists of a triangle, with each corner representing one of the three end members (100% A, 100% B or 100% C) (Figure 4.15a).

To plot a mineral's composition, you need to represent the proportion of each component. In Figure 4.15a, different proportions of component A are represented by lines parallel to the edge BC (0% A). Likewise, different proportions of component B would be represented by lines parallel to the edge CA (0% B), and so on.

To plot a mineral whose composition is: 40% A, 30% B and 30% C, you:

- determine on which 'A' line the 40% composition must lie (as in Figure 4.15a and b)
- find the 30% 'B' line (Figure 4.15b).

The intersection of these two lines at a point marks the composition of the mineral.

As a final check, you can identify the 'C' line, which should pass through the same point (Figure 4.15b).

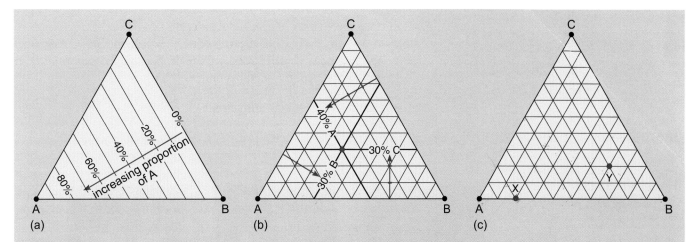

Figure 4.15 (a) A ternary diagram with three end-member components A, B and C. (b) A ternary diagram with the composition $A_{0.4}B_{0.3}C_{0.3}$ plotted. The percentages of the end-member components are indicated by thick lines, which intersect at a point that shows the overall composition. (c) A ternary diagram for use with Question 4.2.

Question 4.2

Using the ABC ternary diagram in Figure 4.15c, determine the compositions indicated by the two points X and Y.

Twinning in feldspar

You were introduced to twinning in Section 2.5. The presence of twinning is a common feature of feldspars and can be a useful diagnostic property.

■ Look at the twinned orthoclase in Figure 4.16a (similar to MS VIII). With reference to the schematic above the specimen, you should be able to see that the crystal is twinned. How are the two twin components related?

☐ The crystal appears to be made of two parts, which look very similar when viewed from different directions – and yet they seem 'squashed' together. These are twin components that overlap with each other (they are said to be inter-penetrant) and are related by a 180° rotation along the long (*z*) axis of the crystal (Figure 4.16a).

This crystal is a kind of growth twin, called a **Carlsbad twin**, which is especially common in K-feldspar. The two twin domains are related by a 180° rotation (Figure 4.16a). Twinning in feldspars does not have to be inter-penetrant and other types of twinning may occur by reflection along twin planes, producing either simple or multiple twinning (Figure 4.16b and c).

How might the feldspars be distinguished? In plane-polarised light, feldspars have low relief and are colourless. Both alkali and plagioclase feldspars are susceptible (though not necessarily under the same conditions) to alteration to fine-grained micas and clay minerals, which often gives them a turbid (dirty-looking) appearance (e.g. Figure 4.17b). However, both plagioclase and alkali feldspars have some distinctive features under the microscope.

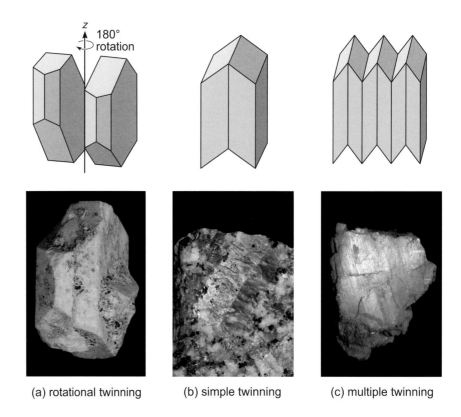

(a) rotational twinning   (b) simple twinning   (c) multiple twinning

Figure 4.16 Twinning in feldspar in schematic form (above) and as seen in hand specimen (below): (a) twinning by rotation – the example here corresponds to Carlsbad twinning (crystal 5 cm high); (b) an example of simple twinning (two twin components) – twinned by reflection (field of view 2 cm across); (c) repeated twin components – twinned by reflection (crystal 3 cm across).

■ Would you expect to be able to see simple twinning in a thin section of a feldspar when viewed with plane-polarised light?

☐ Not normally. There is unlikely to be a significant difference in colour or relief between the two twin components.

■ What would happen if the section were viewed between crossed polars?

☐ On either side of the twin boundary, the crystal orientations would be different. Therefore the adjacent twin domains would go into extinction at different times. As the microscope stage was rotated, first one half of the twin would go into extinction, then the other half (e.g. Figure 4.17c).

Twinning in feldspars is most obvious between crossed polars. In addition to simple twins, plagioclase feldspar often shows repeated or multiple twinning (Figures 4.16c and 4.18a) usually on a microscopic scale, which gives crystals a striped appearance (Figure 4.18c). This is often referred to as **lamellar twinning**, and is a characteristic feature of plagioclase feldspars.

(a)

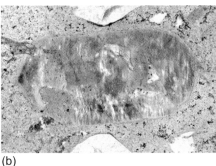
(b)

(c)

Figure 4.17 (a) Alkali feldspar, illustrating penetrative Carlsbad twinning (the reddened crystal is 2 cm long). The pinkish colour is common in alkali feldspar but not diagnostic. (b) Plane-polarised light image of alkali feldspar in a silica-rich lava (field of view 6 mm across). Although the crystal has low relief, the slightly brown, turbid appearance due to alteration is distinctive. (c) The same field of view as in (b) between crossed polars. The alkali feldspar has first-order grey interference colours. The crystal is a simple twin, its twin plane is defined by the slight difference in interference colours (light and dark grey).

(a)

(b)

(c)

Figure 4.18 (a) Plagioclase feldspar, showing lamellar twinning, although this is rarely visible in hand specimen (crystal 4 cm long). (b) Plane-polarised light image of plagioclase in a gabbro. The plagioclase has very low relief and is hard to see, although it lies between the higher relief pyroxene crystals. (c) The same field of view as in (b) between crossed polars, with distinctive zebra-striped lamellar twinning now obvious.

One variety of K-feldspar, known as **microcline**, shows two kinds of repeated twinning in thin section, with one set of twins arranged at 90° to the other set. The lamellar twins overlap each other and have 'fuzzy' edges, giving a 'tartan' appearance known as **cross-hatched twinning** (see Figure 4.19).

Activity 4.6 Simple twinning in orthoclase feldspar

This activity will help you to recognise orthoclase feldspar in thin section.

Figure 4.19 A microcline (K-feldspar) crystal, viewed between crossed polars, displaying classic cross-hatched twinning (field of view 4.8 mm across).

Activity 4.7 Multiple twinning in feldspar

This activity will help you to recognise plagioclase and microcline feldspars in thin section.

Activity 4.8 Zoning in plagioclase

This activity will help you to recognise compositional zoning of crystals as developed in plagioclase feldspar.

4.7 Non-silicate minerals

4.7.1 Carbonates

The most common carbonate mineral is **calcite** ($CaCO_3$) (Figure 4.20a and MS IV). Calcite is one polymorph of $CaCO_3$. Another polymorph is **aragonite**, which has a different crystal structure – it is orthorhombic rather than trigonal. Aragonite is less stable than calcite under ambient conditions. Many marine organisms initially build their skeletons of aragonite but, when they die, their shells drop to the sea floor and gradually the aragonite transforms into calcite.

Calcite is the major constituent of limestone rocks. Limestones are important **industrial minerals**; they are used not only as aggregates in the construction industry and in powdered form as filler for plastics, paints and rubber, but also as a major constituent of cement.

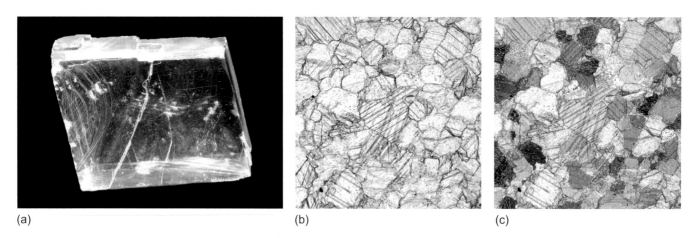

(a) (b) (c)

Figure 4.20 (a) A classic rhombohedral cleavage fragment of calcite (crystal 5 cm across). (b) Plane-polarised light view of calcite crystals in a marble (field of view 2 mm across). Because calcite has high anisotropy, both cleavage and twin planes can be observed in the crystals. (c) The same field of view as in (b) between crossed polars. Calcite has extremely high interference colours and these fourth-order colours have distinctive 'washed-out' pastel tones.

In thin section, calcite is distinctive: it is a highly anisotropic mineral, with high-order interference colours (Figure 4.20c). In hand specimen it is quite a soft mineral (hardness 3 on Mohs' scale, Table 2.2) and has three excellent cleavages (Figure 4.20a). Dilute (5–10%) hydrochloric acid (HCl) provides a good test for calcium carbonate in hand specimen. A few drops, carefully applied, will fizz, giving off carbon dioxide:

$$CaCO_3(s) + 2H^+(aq) = Ca^{2-}(aq) + CO_2(g) + H_2O(l) \qquad (4.1)$$

Dolomite $(CaMg(CO_3)_2)$ is another carbonate mineral that is found in many limestones. Dolomite rocks form when there is an excess of Mg ions available, either during their formation or during later burial.

4.7.2 Oxides

Oxides are an important group of non-silicate minerals. **Hematite** (Fe_2O_3) (MS XI) and **magnetite** (Fe_3O_4) are the two most common oxides of iron. Hematite contains iron in its most oxidised form (Fe^{3+}) and often has a striking red–brown colour similar to rust (hydrated iron oxide) and is responsible for the intense red colour of some desert sandstones. Magnetite and hematite are found in banded iron formation deposits of Precambrian age which are the main sources of iron ore today (Figure 4.21). In most rocks, they are present only as accessory minerals.

Magnetite is a member of the **spinel** group of minerals, which have the general formula AB_2O_4, where A represents 2+ cations and B represents 3+ cations. A large number of elements can substitute into the spinel structure so that spinel group minerals are present in a wide range of igneous, metamorphic and sedimentary rocks. **Chromite** $(FeCr_2O_4)$ is a chrome spinel found in silica-poor igneous rocks and is an important source of chromium.

■ Both hematite and magnetite are opaque minerals. How would you expect them to appear in plane-polarised light and between crossed polars?

☐ Opaque minerals appear black both in plane-polarised light and between crossed polars, which makes specific identification difficult. By contrast, non-opaque *isotropic minerals* are black only when between crossed polars – which is an important distinction.

Figure 4.21 Typical sample of a banded iron formation deposit, the main source of iron ore (specimen 11 cm across).

4.7.3 Sulfides

Sulfur is an essential constituent of sulfide minerals, in which it commonly bonds with metals such as copper, lead and zinc. Sulfides can be important economically when they are concentrated in mineral deposits. They often occur as vein mineralisation, deposited by hot, watery fluids passing through fractures, fault zones and permeable rocks (Box 6.1). Some are formed by segregation processes in sulfur-rich magmatic systems. Mining followed by smelting of the sulfide minerals allows the metals to be extracted. Examples of economically important sulfide mineral deposits include the Pb–Zn deposits of the Mississippi Valley and the vast disseminated Cu deposits of the Andes.

Pyrite (FeS_2) (Figure 4.22a and MS I) is the most commonly encountered sulfide mineral in vein deposits and is also found in igneous, metamorphic and sedimentary rocks. Other common sulfide minerals in vein deposits include **galena** (PbS) (Figure 4.22b and MS VI), sphalerite (ZnS) (Figure 2.14c) and **chalcopyrite** ($CuFeS_2$).

(a)   (b)

Figure 4.22   (a) Pyrite (3 cm across). (b) Galena (7 cm across).

4.8   Summary of Chapter 4

1   The most important rock-forming minerals on Earth are silicate minerals, composed of silicon, oxygen and a variety of metal cations. The basic building block of silicate minerals is the SiO_4 tetrahedron. However, what defines the structural variety and with it a range of properties of silicate minerals is the ability of SiO_4 tetrahedra to link together, or polymerise, by sharing oxygen atoms in different ways and in different proportions. Increasing polymerisation increases the silicon to oxygen ratio to reach that of quartz, which has a fully polymerised structure.

2   Silicate mineral groups are built of different forms of three-dimensional structure: isolated units, chains, sheets and frameworks, with a corresponding increase in the silicon to oxygen ratio from 1 : 4 to 1 : 2. These three-dimensional structures are mostly bound together by metal cations. The crystal structures of these mineral groups have important consequences for the physical properties of the minerals.

3   The main silicate mineral groups covered in this section, for which the chemistry, structure, occurrence and properties are considered, are those with isolated SiO_4 tetrahedra (olivine and garnet), the chain silicates

(pyroxene and amphibole), the sheet silicates (micas and clay minerals) and the framework silicates (quartz and feldspar). The diagnostic properties of minerals in thin section are summarised on *Reference Card 1*.

4   Major non-silicate mineral groups include the carbonates, oxides and sulfides. Carbonates are an important part of the carbon cycle whereby carbonate minerals are precipitated from seawater, often as skeletons of organisms, and deposited on the sea floor. Oxide and sulfide minerals can be economically important as sources of metals when they are concentrated as mineral deposits.

4.9   Objectives for Chapter 4

Now you have completed this chapter, you should be able to:

4.1 Summarise the range of silicate mineral structures in terms of various degrees of SiO_4 polymerisation.

4.2 Outline the essential structural features of the common rock-forming minerals: olivine, garnet, pyroxene, amphibole, mica, quartz and feldspar.

4.3 Give examples of some physical properties of minerals that can be attributed to specific crystal structural features.

4.4 Describe the basic chemistry and properties of common rock-forming minerals in the Home Kit (with the aid of information summarised on *Reference Card 1*).

4.5 Describe the distinguishing features of the major rock-forming minerals in hand specimen and thin section (with the aid of information summarised on *Reference Card 1*).

Now try the following questions to test your understanding of Chapter 4.

Question 4.3

The structure of quartz is built entirely of SiO_4 units. Why, then, is its chemical formula SiO_2?

Question 4.4

Quartz and mica are both silicate minerals, but they have very different cleavage properties. How do quartz and mica differ in this respect, and why?

Question 4.5

What is meant by solid solution? Give two examples of important rock-forming minerals that exhibit solid solution.

Crystaline — Made of Crystals

Fragmental — Made of fragments of existing Rock

Crystaline has a mass of interlocking crystals grown together

Pleochroism = PPL = Changes Colour

Chapter 5 Introducing rocks

You have studied a range of common minerals and have seen how many of their properties and characteristics relate to their internal atomic structure and chemistry. In this chapter, you will extend the scope and scale of your studies to rocks, which are consolidated, natural materials, usually comprising aggregates of mineral grains. In subsequent chapters, you will learn about the main types of rocks found on Earth, their mineral constituents and their occurrence. Careful observation of rocks is crucial for working out how they formed.

- ■ What names are given to the three main types of rocks, and how is each formed? (Refer back to Section 1.1 if you are unsure.)

- ☐ The three main rock types are igneous, sedimentary and metamorphic.

  Igneous rocks are formed by solidification of magma at or beneath the Earth's surface.

  Sedimentary rocks are formed at the Earth's surface, mostly by the accumulation, in various ways, of rock, mineral and organic debris; some are formed by precipitation of minerals when salty water evaporates.

  Metamorphic rocks are formed beneath the Earth's surface when any type of rock is changed by temperature and/or pressure to form new minerals, which are usually quite different from the original ones.

5.1 Rock textures

When attempting to identify a rock, it is often useful to examine the rock's **texture** before examining the minerals of which it is made, because this can often give clues as to its likely origin. Texture is the term used to describe the physical character of the constituents that make up a rock and how those constituents are arranged, such as whether they are made of interlocking and intergrown crystals or comprise layers of accumulated fragments. Texture is often visible to the naked eye, but it can be invaluable to view rocks at progressively enlarged scales using a hand lens or microscope (as illustrated in Figure 5.1). Minerals may be recognisable in hand specimen, especially in coarse-grained rocks, but it often requires a hand lens to distinguish them, especially the smaller grains, and microscopic examination of a thin section is required to confirm mineral identification and distinguish very small grains.

Activity 5.1 Using the microscope

In this activity, you will learn about the use of the polarising microscope for identifying minerals and developing a better understanding of rocks.

Most rocks have textures that are either crystalline (i.e. made of crystals) or **fragmental** (i.e. made of fragments of existing rock, including mineral

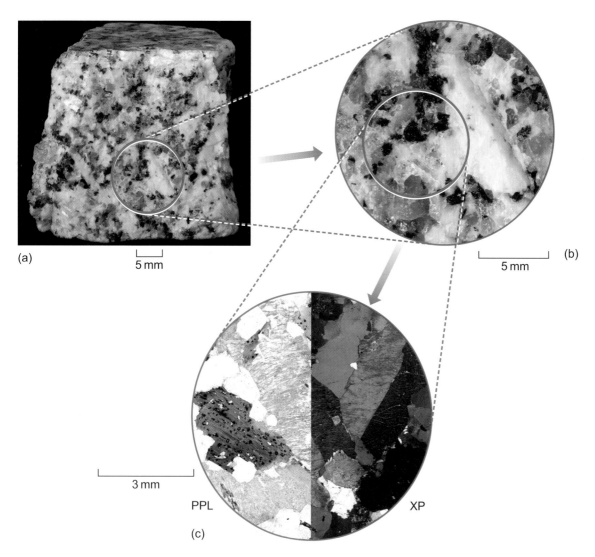

(a)

5 mm

(b)

5 mm

3 mm

PPL

XP

(c)

Figure 5.1 Observation of rocks at various scales for comprehensive description and effective interpretation: (a) rock specimen (viewed with the naked eye); (b) close-up of the rock surface (as seen through a hand lens); (c) thin section (viewed through a microscope in plane-polarised light (PPL) and between crossed polars (XP)).

grains). Although the recognition of texture is not an infallible guide to rock type, this broad textural division is a useful starting point.

In rocks with a crystalline texture, the minerals have *grown* together to form a mass of interlocking crystals. In most rocks with a fragmental texture, individual mineral and rock fragments (the grains often somewhat rounded during transportation) have been *assembled* as a result of deposition. Within both textural categories, the size of individual fragments or crystals can vary considerably. Rocks with a crystalline texture are usually harder and stronger than those with a fragmental texture, and when they are broken they tend to fracture *across* crystals, often along mineral cleavage planes (Figures 5.2a and b), resulting in flat areas on fracture surfaces that reflect and glint as they catch the light. Rocks with a fragmental texture tend to fracture along paths occupied by the softer, finer-grained matrix *around* larger individual grains (Figure 5.2c). If the grains are rigidly held together, for example by a natural mineral **cement** that has precipitated from solutions percolating through the rock, then the grains may themselves break.

Simple observations of texture can indicate to which major group of rocks a specimen belongs.

- A rock that consists of interlocking crystals in random orientations (e.g. Figure 5.2a) is likely to have formed when minerals grew together during the crystallisation of a magma. This would be an igneous rock (Chapter 6).

  Igneous – Interlocking Crystals

- A rock that is composed of a mixture of grains – possibly some rounded, some more angular, some as mineral grains, and others as fragments of rock (e.g. Figure 5.2c) – is likely to have been a sediment that has become consolidated to form a sedimentary rock (Chapter 7).

  Sedimentary

- A rock that has a crystalline texture but with individual crystals strongly aligned in one direction (e.g. Figure 5.2b) is unlikely to have been derived by crystallisation from a magma. It probably formed as a result of the growth of minerals in the solid state under conditions of intense, directed pressure. This rock, therefore, is likely to be metamorphic (Chapter 8).

  Metamorphic

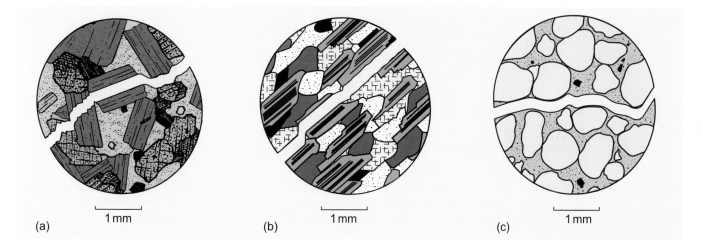

(a)   1 mm   (b)   1 mm   (c)   1 mm

Figure 5.2 Examples of the fracture patterns displayed by rocks: (a) crystalline texture in random orientation; (b) crystalline texture with strong crystal alignment; (c) fragmental texture.

Activity 5.2   Crystalline and fragmental textures

In this activity, you will examine and compare crystalline and fragmental textures of rocks in hand specimen and thin section.

Chapters 6 to 8 will introduce you to the major rock types and their classification. Be aware, though, that rocks do not always fit neatly into convenient pigeonholes; they contain a range of different minerals and in varying proportions, so it may not always be possible to give a specific name to a rock specimen. This does not matter; it is preferable to make careful observations that lead to a valid interpretation, rather than to memorise lists of names and characteristics. 'Instant recognition' comes only with familiarity and practice, using the skills you will develop throughout this course. At times, even experienced geologists can be unsure of the best name to give a particular rock specimen and need to use sophisticated methods to help in identification.

Chapters 6 to 8 will also demonstrate how accurate *observation* of the texture and the constituents of a rock can be used to deduce the *process* by which it was formed and hence interpret its *environment* of formation (Section 1.1). Such deductions also have implications on a larger scale, for interpreting the geological history of the area in which the rocks occur. But before investigating the main types of rocks more thoroughly, it is worth considering how natural rock-forming processes recycle the materials of which rocks are made.

5.2   The rock cycle

Rocks are continually being created, modified and destroyed by geological processes of many kinds, operating at all scales, from that of a mineral grain decomposing during weathering, to oceanic crust being formed as a result of plate tectonic processes. A neat way of viewing how different types of rocks may be interrelated by the processes that form and re-form them is through a conceptual system known as the **rock cycle**.

The rock cycle (Figure 5.3) not only sets the three main groups of rocks into a spatial context, but also links them through processes of transformation. External processes at the Earth's surface include weathering, transportation and deposition, as well as biological processes such as the growth of organisms. The Earth's internal processes include burial and subsidence, which may lead to metamorphism and, potentially, to magma generation. Weathering, erosion and sediment deposition are closely linked to another important system, known as the water cycle, or **hydrological cycle**, which describes the movement and distribution of water at the Earth's surface and is driven by both gravity and the heat from the Sun (Figure 5.4).

5.2.1   Processes of the rock cycle

As illustrated schematically in Figure 5.3, weathering and erosion of all rocks exposed at the Earth's surface give rise to soluble and insoluble products. These materials are transported across the land surface by water, wind and ice, mostly to be deposited as sediments in seas and oceans. With progressive accumulation, sediments are buried and can be **lithified** (or hardened) by compaction and cementation to form sedimentary rocks. These rocks, or indeed any kind of rock, may be uplifted by tectonic processes and exposed by weathering and erosion at the Earth's surface, thus providing materials for new sedimentary rocks. However, when subjected to burial and subsidence, or to Earth movements associated with mountain building, then the increase in pressure and/or temperature can transform them into metamorphic rocks. At extremely high temperatures metamorphic rocks may melt to give magma, and, in sufficient quantities, magma that is less dense than the surrounding

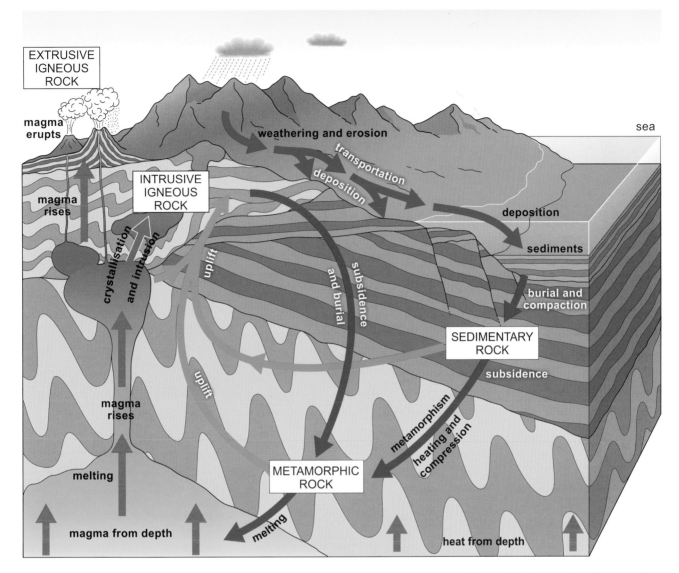

Figure 5.3 The rock cycle showing schematically the relationships between the Earth's internal and external processes and the three major rock groups that can be transformed from one to another.

rocks will rise within the crust and eventually solidify at or beneath the Earth's surface as igneous rocks. However, metamorphic rocks may be uplifted and exposed at the Earth's surface without melting having occurred. In these various ways, material is continually, albeit very slowly, moving around the rock cycle. In fact, given suitable geological conditions, any igneous, sedimentary or metamorphic rock may be:

*   weathered and eroded to provide the material for sedimentary rocks

*   metamorphosed into a new metamorphic rock

*   melted to form magma and new igneous rocks.

■   What processes of the rock cycle would be involved in transforming (a) an extrusive igneous rock into a sedimentary rock, and (b) a sedimentary rock into an intrusive igneous rock?

☐ Although there could be various possible routes around the rock cycle, probably these are the simplest: (a) the extrusive igneous rock is weathered and/or eroded; the products are transported to a site of deposition where they accumulate to form sediments; the sediments undergo burial and compaction during which they become lithified to form sedimentary rock; (b) the sedimentary rock is melted by intense heat during deep burial to form magma, but unless the heating is very rapid, metamorphism would occur before melting. The magma would rise into cooler rocks and crystallise to form an intrusive igneous rock.

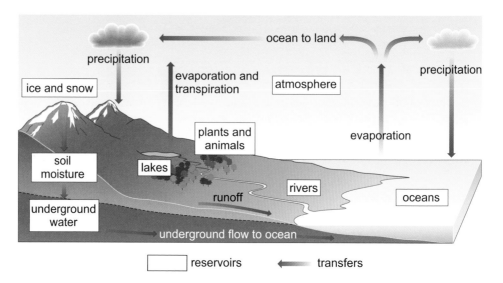

Figure 5.4 The hydrological cycle, illustrating the natural movement of water at the Earth's surface.

Although the rock cycle is basically a simple scheme, it may seem rather complicated because of the variety of routes through which rock materials can travel around it and be transformed. Many of these stages, such as the formation of metamorphic rock, can take vast amounts of time. Remarkably, the various constituents of an individual rock can be derived from a large number of different sources (Section 1.1). The rock cycle demonstrates that rocks and rock-forming processes are interlinked, which leads to continuous recycling of the materials that comprise the Earth's crust and uppermost mantle.

5.3 Summary of Chapter 5

1 Rocks are consolidated natural materials, usually comprising aggregates of mineral grains.

2 Identifying a rock sample and deducing its origin requires observation at different scales: from visual examination with the naked eye, to enlargement with a hand lens, to observation of thin sections using a polarising microscope.

3 Texture is the term used to describe the physical relationship between the constituent materials of which a rock is made. In rocks with a crystalline

texture, minerals have grown together to form interlocking crystals. In most rocks with a fragmental texture, mineral grains and rock fragments have been transported and deposited before consolidation.

4   The main rock groups can usually be recognised on the basis of their textural properties: igneous rocks are crystalline, mostly with randomly oriented minerals; most sedimentary rocks contain fragmental grains; and metamorphic rocks are crystalline, mostly with minerals exhibiting a strong preferred orientation. There are exceptions, however, that will be considered in later chapters.

5   Rocks of all kinds are continually being created, modified and destroyed by geological processes, such as weathering, erosion and deposition, magma generation and metamorphism, all of which are linked together within the conceptual system of the rock cycle.

6   Weathering, erosion and sediment deposition are linked to the hydrological cycle, which governs the movement and availability of water at the Earth's surface. The hydrological cycle is driven by energy from the Sun.

7   Given suitable geological conditions, any igneous, sedimentary or metamorphic rock can be weathered and eroded to provide the material for sedimentary rocks; may be metamorphosed into a new metamorphic rock; or even melted to form magma and new igneous rocks.

5.4   Objectives for Chapter 5

Now you have completed this chapter, you should be able to:

5.1 Describe and explain the differences between crystalline and fragmental rock textures.

5.2 Outline the differences in the origins and typical textures of igneous, sedimentary and metamorphic rocks.

5.3 Explain the concept of the rock cycle.

5.4 Relate the three major rock groups to their relative positions in the rock cycle.

Chapter 6   Igneous rocks

For millennia, people living near volcanoes have noticed that when red-hot molten lava erupts onto the Earth's surface and cools, it solidifies to form rock. You may have seen volcanoes while holidaying abroad, perhaps on the Canary Islands or in Italy, and there are often spectacular images of volcanic eruptions on TV news and documentary programmes. Rocks formed by volcanic eruption (known as extrusive igneous rocks) are not the only rocks formed by the cooling and crystallisation of magma, much of which occurs deep beneath the Earth's surface to form intrusive igneous rocks. In this chapter, you will consider how observations of texture, the grain size of crystals, and the mineral and chemical compositions of igneous rocks are linked to the geological conditions in which they are found. This will help not only in describing and classifying different types of igneous rocks, but also in deducing the circumstances of their formation.

6.1   Cooling of magmas and the grain size of igneous rocks

As magmas cool and begin to solidify, the atoms in the liquid organise themselves to form crystals of different mineral compositions. Any small disturbance in the melt, such as specks of impurity or slight turbulence, may be sufficient for the first tiny crystals to start to form. These sites are known as **nucleation centres**. Individual crystals continue to grow in an ordered fashion by the successive addition of atoms to their faces, according to the geometry of the crystal structure (Section 2.6). As the crystals are growing in a liquid, they will generally be in random orientation relative to one another. The larger the number of nucleation centres in the melt, the more crystals will form. Sooner or later, with continued growth, the crystals will come into contact with one another and develop interlocking boundaries, which is typical of most igneous rocks.

■   Figure 6.1a–c shows three dark igneous rocks. What is the most obvious difference between them?

☐   Their grain size. **Gabbro** is coarse grained, with individual grains clearly visible; **dolerite** is medium grained – individual grains are just discernible; and **basalt** is fine grained, with only a few individual grains distinguishable. Yet in chemical and mineralogical composition these rocks are very similar. (See also RS 19, RS 14 and RS 3, and the Digital Kit.)

Activity 6.1   Grain size and cooling rates in igneous rocks

This activity will help you understand how the grain size of igneous rocks enables you to make deductions about their cooling history.

Figure 6.1 Examples of three dark igneous rocks: (a) gabbro (7 cm); (b) dolerite (7.5 cm); (c) basalt (4 cm). Typical occurrences are, respectively: (d) the Cuillin Hills, Isle of Skye; (e) an intrusive sheet of dolerite at Clee Hill, Shropshire; (f) outlines of basalt columns (about 30 cm across) on the surface of a lava flow, Isle of Staffa.

The Cuillin Hills of Skye (Figure 6.1d) are composed of gabbro and probably represent the remains of a large reservoir of magma or **magma chamber** that cooled slowly and may have once formed the root of a huge extinct volcano, now eroded away. The dolerite crystallised more quickly, in this case as part of a sheet-like body intruded between layers of sedimentary rocks at Clee Hill, Shropshire (Figure 6.1e). Basalt commonly forms lava flows, which may, on cooling, develop a spectacular polygonal pattern of **columnar joints**, such as those found at Fingal's Cave on the Isle of Staffa (Figure 6.1f) and the Giant's Causeway in County Antrim, Northern Ireland.

Figure 6.1a–c shows that the appearance of igneous rocks of similar chemical and mineral composition can be quite different according to their grain size, ranging from coarse to fine. Although this may seem to be a fairly arbitrary means of classification, the criteria used to describe grain size in igneous rocks can be quantified (see Table 6.1) according to the *average* grain size of the **groundmass** or matrix minerals. This classification ignores the size of any large isolated crystals.

Table 6.1 Grain-size criteria for classifying igneous rocks. Note that the divisions are made according to the *average* grain size of the groundmass or matrix minerals.

Classification	Size	Appearance
coarse-grained	>2 mm	crystals easily seen with the naked eye
medium-grained	0.25–2 mm	crystals usually just visible with the naked eye; easily seen with a hand lens
fine-grained	<0.25 mm	crystals barely distinguishable, or indistinguishable, with a hand lens

Grain size in igneous rocks is partly determined by the number of nucleation centres in the crystallising magma. It also depends on the rate at which atoms are able to migrate (or diffuse) towards these nuclei. Rates of diffusion are greatest at high temperatures when the magma is also more mobile, and lowest at low temperatures when it is also more viscous (sticky). So, when magma cools slowly, and the temperature remains high for long enough, long-range migration of atoms is possible, encouraging the growth of large crystals (as in the gabbro, Figure 6.1a).

■ Under what conditions would such slow cooling of magma occur?

☐ Slow cooling occurs when magma is intruded deep beneath the Earth's surface into rocks that are themselves quite hot and able to insulate the magma.

Conversely, when a magma cools quickly, the decrease in diffusion rate inhibits the migration of atoms and a large number of nucleation centres develop, resulting in numerous small crystals.

So, as a general rule, in most igneous rocks:

• the coarser the grain size, the slower the cooling (at depth) has been

• the finer the grain size, the faster the cooling (at or near the surface) has been.

With extremely fast cooling, atoms may not arrange themselves to form crystals, in which case a glass is formed (Section 2.2). Sometimes, tiny scattered crystals form at nucleation centres, and the remaining liquid solidifies as a glass (Figure 6.2).

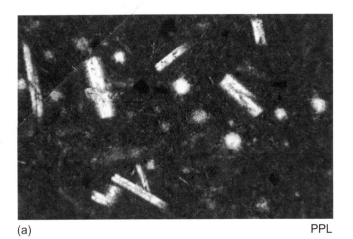
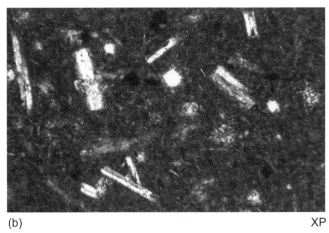

(a)   PPL   (b)   XP

Figure 6.2 Photomicrograph of a thin section of an igneous rock that has cooled so quickly that only a few crystals formed before the remaining liquid solidified as glass, which appears (a) brown in plane-polarised light, and (b) isotropic (dark) between crossed polars. Field of view approximately 2 mm wide.

■   What is the characteristic optical property of a glass under the microscope?

□   Glass (both natural and artificial) is isotropic, i.e. it remains dark when viewed between crossed polars as the stage is rotated (Section 3.3.2).

Figure 6.3a shows a rock called **obsidian**, which consists entirely of natural glass. It is black and shiny, with a characteristic curved or conchoidal fracture (see also the Digital Kit) just like that seen in broken blocks of manufactured glass. You might think that natural glass would be clear and colourless like window glass; however, just as manufactured glass can be produced in a wide range of colours, the black colour is probably due to minor components such as iron, which can dramatically affect its colour. Clear glass has to be made from an artificial silicate melt created from carefully selected ingredients that include very pure silica sand to ensure it lacks colour; the melt must be cooled so rapidly that it does not crystallise at all. As discussed in Section 2.2, glass is not particularly stable over a very long timescale and will eventually crystallise (**devitrify**) with age. This can sometimes be observed in natural glasses such as obsidian (Figure 6.3b).

The igneous rocks that you have looked at so far have been even grained or **equigranular**, the individual mineral grains in each rock being more or less the same size. However, in some igneous rocks, relatively large crystals, known as **phenocrysts**, are set in a finer-grained groundmass (Figure 6.4). The texture of such rocks is described as **porphyritic**.

(a)

(b)

Figure 6.3 (a) The volcanic glass, obsidian (10 cm), which forms when silica-rich lava cools too rapidly for crystals to form. Note the characteristic black appearance and the curved fracture surfaces. (b) Partially devitrified (snowflake) obsidian (11 cm) in which crystals form locally as a result of devitrification and show up as white spots and layers.

Figure 6.4 A porphyritic igneous rock (4 cm) with large crystals set in a finer-grained matrix or groundmass. (See also RS 6.)

Question 6.1

What does the variation in grain size of the rock shown in Figure 6.4 indicate about the cooling history of the rock and the mobility of atoms in the magma?

Activity 6.2   Phenocrysts in porphyritic rocks

This activity will help you to understand the crystallisation history of porphyritic rocks.

6.2   Crystallisation of magmas: mineralogy and composition

Magmas are complex chemical mixtures, containing many elements that become distributed among a number of minerals as the magma crystallises. Usually, each mineral in an igneous rock *begins* to crystallise at a different temperature, so it is not surprising that igneous textures can be complex. The essential point to remember is that, in most cases, a magma crystallises over a *range* of temperatures and does not solidify all at once. This is particularly well demonstrated in porphyritic rocks (e.g. Figure 6.4) in which the cooling rate must have been slow at first before becoming much more rapid. The minerals forming the phenocrysts do not stop crystallising; indeed, the groundmass minerals of a porphyritic rock often include those that form the phenocrysts.

It is frequently possible to work out the order of crystallisation of minerals in igneous rocks by examining relationships between crystals in a thin section. Figure 6.5 is a photomicrograph (photograph of a thin section) of a gabbro similar to that in Figure 6.1a. You should be able to see plagioclase feldspar crystals (usually as elongate, rectangular shapes with first-order interference colours and lamellar twinning) enclosed within large pyroxene crystals (occupying a large area and with second-order yellowish interference colours).

■ What evidence is there that at least some of the plagioclase crystallised *before* the pyroxene? (*Hint:* consider the location of plagioclase relative to pyroxene crystals.)

☐ The irregular pyroxene crystals *enclose* the long, thin plagioclase crystals. As the magma cooled, therefore, at least some of the plagioclase must have crystallised *before* the pyroxene.

The answer to this last question illustrates a general rule regarding the crystallisation history of an igneous rock:

• When one crystal encloses another, the enclosed crystal formed first.

In Figure 6.5, it is clear that the plagioclase crystals are generally both smaller and more numerous than the pyroxene crystals. However, the rock is not porphyritic because, although the pyroxene crystals are large, they have grown *after* the plagioclase feldspars. The pyroxene is not a phenocryst. The magma probably cooled slowly, more or less steadily during its solidification.

Figure 6.5 Thin section of gabbro, viewed under a microscope between crossed polars. Field of view about 3 mm.

The fundamental control on the mineral composition of an igneous rock is the chemistry of the magma from which it has crystallised. As a magma begins to cool, its composition determines which mineral crystallises first. At progressively lower temperatures, other minerals begin to crystallise. Those that started crystallising at higher temperatures may continue or cease to crystallise. The temperature ranges over which the **major minerals** of igneous rocks generally form during the cooling of a magma are summarised in Figure 6.6.

Diagrams such as Figure 6.6 are based on the results of experimental studies of the conditions (especially temperature) under which igneous rocks form. The 'lozenge' shapes give some idea as to which minerals crystallise at a given temperature; the relative importance of each mineral in a crystallising assemblage varies as the magma cools. Where the widest part of a 'lozenge' lies within a field corresponding to a particular rock type, the mineral can be regarded as a major mineral of that rock. Minerals present in very small amounts, especially oxide, sulfide and phosphate minerals, are called **accessory minerals**. Note that the ranges for several minerals do not overlap at all (e.g. those of muscovite and pyroxene; quartz and olivine). Where such gaps exist, those minerals are very rarely found together in igneous rocks.

Thus olivine is hardly ever found with quartz or potassium feldspar. In contrast, minerals whose ranges of crystallisation temperatures overlap are commonly found together, so that olivine, pyroxene and Ca-rich plagioclase feldspar commonly occur in association – as in gabbros. The associations shown in Figure 6.6, therefore, can form the basis for a simple igneous rock classification.

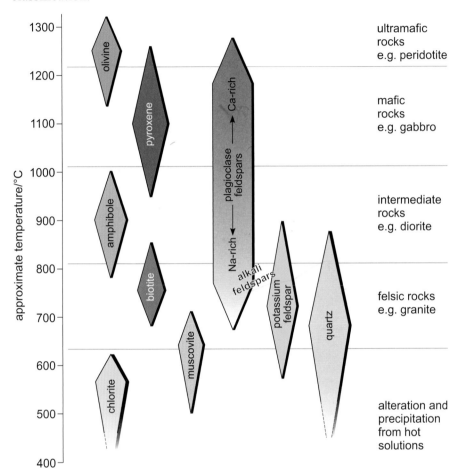

Figure 6.6 Approximate crystallisation temperature ranges for common minerals in igneous rocks, showing the mineral associations (for given temperature ranges) commonly found in igneous rocks.

Activity 6.3 Groundmass minerals in a porphyritic rock
This activity compares the groundmass constituents with the phenocrysts.

6.3 Intrusive rocks

Most intrusive igneous rocks form by relatively slow crystallisation of magmas. This occurs either at depth in the crust as large intrusions or **plutons**, or nearer the surface in cracks and fractures as shallow **minor**

intrusions, such as dykes or sills. Dykes are sheet-like igneous bodies that cut *across* pre-existing rock layers, i.e. they are **discordant**. **Sills** are also sheet-like but, by contrast, are intruded *between* the layers of pre-existing rocks, i.e. they are **concordant** (Figure 6.7a), although there may be an occasional discordant step across layers (Figure 6.7b). Dykes (often near vertical) and sills (often near horizontal) are generally offshoots from deeper magma chambers and may be associated with surface volcanoes and lava flows.

(a)

(b)

Figure 6.7 (a) A concordant sill of basaltic composition intruding layered sedimentary rocks, Beacon Valley, Transantarctic Mountains, Antarctica. (b) A schematic cross-section showing the difference between a dyke and a sill and their relationship to a magma chamber at depth and to surface volcanism.

As you have seen, Figure 6.6 shows the temperature ranges over which the major minerals found in the main plutonic rock types crystallise. Note that the long plagioclase feldspar 'lozenge' embodies the gradational change in composition of plagioclase crystallising at different temperatures: from relatively Ca-rich compositions in high-temperature magmas (gabbroic), through intermediate varieties with similar amounts of Ca and Na in their mineral structure (dioritic), to Na-rich varieties in low-temperature magmas (granitic).

- ■ Based on Figure 6.6, what major minerals would you expect to find in a diorite?

- ☐ Mostly amphibole and plagioclase feldspar (intermediate in composition between the Ca- and Na-rich varieties), along with either biotite or pyroxene (though not usually both). Potassium feldspar and/or quartz also occur in some diorites.

Activity 6.4   Essential minerals in the main types of plutonic rock

This activity involves examination of thin sections using the Virtual Microscope and will help reinforce your knowledge of the mineral constituents of intrusive igneous rocks.

Figure 6.8 shows an important coarse-grained igneous rock, known as **peridotite**. It comprises olivine, pyroxene and some (Ca-rich) plagioclase, a high-temperature mineral association (Figure 6.6), formed near the base of some igneous intrusions by the accumulation of early-formed, dense, high-temperature minerals. Although not very common at the Earth's surface, it is an important rock because it is similar to the mantle material that underlies the Earth's crust and from which basaltic magmas are derived.

Figure 6.8   Example of peridotite (3.3 cm), similar to the rock that typically forms much of the Earth's mantle. (See also RS 23 and the Digital Kit.)

Activity 6.5   Mineralogy of peridotite

This activity examines peridotite, another important coarse-grained igneous rock.

The mineralogy of the three plutonic igneous rock types, gabbro, diorite and granite, is shown in Figure 6.6. Because they are coarse grained, these rock types would have crystallised slowly deep in the crust as large intrusions. However, magmas of these same compositions may also be intruded into cracks and fractures nearer the Earth's surface where they form minor intrusions, such as dykes or sills, which cooled more rapidly than their plutonic counterparts. These rocks are likely to be medium grained in texture, namely dolerite, **microdiorite** and **microgranite**, respectively. The relationships between these rock names are shown in Table 6.2, along with their fine-grained equivalents that may be present in rapidly cooled intrusions, but more commonly in extrusive, volcanic rocks (Section 6.4). Any of these rocks may also be porphyritic. Figure 6.4, for example, shows phenocrysts of quartz and potassium feldspar (orthoclase) in a much finer-grained groundmass, the phenocrysts having crystallised more slowly in a magma chamber at depth before the magma rose and was cooled rapidly. Any remaining liquid would then have crystallised more quickly to form the groundmass. This rock can be classified as a porphyritic rhyolite (Table 6.2).

Table 6.2 Rock names of common igneous rocks.

	Typical occurrence		
	Plutonic	**Shallow intrusive**	**Volcanic**
average grain size of groundmass	coarse (>2 mm)	medium (0.25–2 mm)	fine (<0.25 mm)
	gabbro	dolerite	basalt
	diorite	microdiorite	andesite
	granite	microgranite	rhyolite

Note that any of these rocks may also be porphyritic. For example, a basalt with phenocrysts would be called a 'porphyritic basalt'.

6.4 Extrusive rocks

When magma erupts at the surface, it may spill out as a lava flow (Figure 6.9a). If, however, it is erupted under pressure, it can be blown apart by escaping gases as it is solidifying and be dispersed as fragments of various sizes (Figure 6.9b). When this fragmental debris eventually settles and becomes consolidated, it forms a **pyroclastic** rock. Differences in the composition, gas content and crystallisation temperature of different magmas have considerable influence on their eruptive style.

(a)

(b)

Figure 6.9 (a) A lava flow, Hawaii; (b) a pyroclastic eruption, Montserrat.

Figure 6.10 shows three examples of lava: basalt, **andesite** and **rhyolite**. (See also RS 3, RS 1, and RS 6 (groundmass).) These are the fine-grained compositional equivalents of the plutonic rocks gabbro, diorite and granite, respectively (Table 6.2).

Question 6.2

What textural evidence would you expect to find to show that these three rocks are volcanic in origin?

Basalt lavas tend to be more common than gabbro intrusions, particularly at the Earth's surface, mainly because basaltic magma is very hot and runny and escapes easily up faults and fissures. In contrast, rhyolite lavas tend to be less common than granite plutons, mainly because granite magma is much cooler and viscous, making it more difficult to find its way to the surface, and when it does, it often erupts in an explosive fashion and becomes fragmented, giving rise to pyroclastic deposits.

Figure 6.11 shows a pyroclastic rock, known as an **ignimbrite** (see also RS 25 and the Digital Kit). The sharp, angular outlines of individual minerals and the presence of broken crystals and igneous rock fragments, all in chaotic, random orientation, are evidence of the explosive nature of the eruption that produced this rock. These fragments are surrounded by glassy groundmass material, which indicates very rapid chilling of magma, though some banding and streaking to form a flow-like texture indicates that the material must still have been very hot and 'plastic' before it became consolidated.

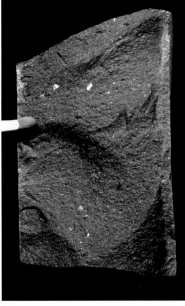

(a)

(b)

(c)

Figure 6.10 Examples of lava: (a) basalt (8 cm); (b) andesite (4.5 cm); (c) rhyolite (10 cm).

Figure 6.11 Ignimbrite (4.5 cm), with fragments of crystals and rock, demonstrating its explosive origin.

Activity 6.6 Pyroclastic textures

Features of pyroclastic rocks, seen best in thin section, are the focus of this activity.

(a)

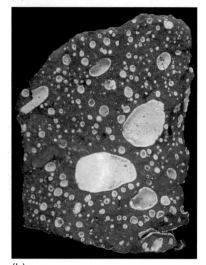

(b)

Figure 6.12 (a) Basalt containing abundant vesicles, the spaces occupied by gas bubbles when lava solidifies; and (b) amygdales in lava from Tenerife, where the vesicles are encrusted (part filled) by minerals deposited by percolating solutions. Maximum length of the specimen in (a) is 3.5 cm and in (b) 6 cm.

Some magmas contain dissolved gases that expand upon eruption to form gas bubbles, which remain in the solidified lava as rounded, smooth-edged, sometimes spherical but often elongate or even sinuous holes, known as **vesicles** (Figure 6.12a). On burial, groundwaters may deposit low-temperature minerals such as quartz (especially agate), calcite and a group of minerals known as **zeolites** in the holes. These cavity fillings are known as **amygdales** (Figure 6.12b).

6.5 Pegmatites and aplites

At high pressures, some granitic magmas contain significant amounts of water – in the extreme, up to 10% by mass, but usually much less. Other volatile components, such as fluorine and boron, may also be present. On crystallisation, some of this water is incorporated into hydrous minerals, such as micas, which contain OH groups in their structures. However, many silicate minerals, in particular quartz and feldspar, are **anhydrous** (i.e. without water in their structures).

■ What happens to the proportion of water in a magma when anhydrous minerals crystallise out?

□ The water remains in an ever-decreasing amount of magma and, therefore, its proportion increases.

If the concentration of water then becomes too high and the confining pressure is insufficient to hold it in the magma, it separates out in the form of an aqueous fluid. In volcanic environments it may simply escape as steam. It can also be a source of hydrothermal deposits (Box 6.1). Under pressure, water-enriched (volatile) magmas of granitic composition are very mobile – unlike most granite magmas, which are viscous. Such fluid magmas can penetrate fractures in the surrounding rock or within the body of the pluton itself to form pegmatite veins. The presence of high concentrations of volatiles (e.g. water, fluorine and boron) and alkali metals (e.g. lithium, Li; rubidium, Rb; and caesium, Cs) in the magma increases diffusion rates and encourages the growth of unusually large, well-formed crystals during cooling. In some spectacular examples, crystals may reach several metres in length. Occupying fractures, such sheets or **veins** of coarse-grained crystals are known as **pegmatites** (Figure 6.13a). Although the term pegmatite refers to the coarse texture rather than the composition, most pegmatites are of a composition similar to some granites. The presence of unusual elements, often with special properties, such as Li, Cs, Rb, tantalum (Ta), niobium (Nb) and tungsten (W), in some pegmatites has led to them being of economic importance (for example, Ta is in demand for electrical capacitors, especially as used in mobile phones). However, most deposits are relatively small and, with today's emphasis on economies of scale, they are now less important economically. It should be emphasised that in pegmatites the large crystal size is *not* simply the result of slow cooling, but the result of crystals being able to grow relatively quickly to a large size because the presence of volatiles in the melt facilitates rapid migration of atoms towards nucleation centres and reduces the temperature at which crystallisation occurs. However, if the aqueous fluid separates and escapes under pressure along cracks, rapid crystallisation of the remaining melt occurs, leading to the formation of veins of a fine-grained, equigranular (sugary-textured) rock known as **aplite** (Figure 6.13b), which is particularly rich in feldspar and quartz.

(a)

Box 6.1 Hydrothermal ore deposits

Hot aqueous (**hydrothermal**) solutions, sometimes of igneous origin themselves, are often associated with areas of crust heated by igneous activity. Their importance is due to their role in the formation of mineralised deposits that may be sufficiently rich in metalliferous (metal-bearing) minerals to form valuable hydrothermal **ore deposits**. A wide range of aqueous solutions may take part in ore deposit formation: cool, shallow groundwaters and seawater; warm solutions of more deeply circulating groundwaters (as in mineral and hot spring areas); and extremely hot solutions associated with the deepest fluids released by metamorphic reactions or as by-products of magma crystallisation.

Aqueous fluids at high temperatures (above about 400 °C) and at high pressure are highly reactive and highly mobile. They are able to leach out elements from wall rocks, may even dissolve minerals, and can penetrate even the narrowest rock fractures. As the fluids migrate along fractures away from where they originated, not only do the temperature and pressure conditions change, but the fluids are likely to react chemically with the surrounding rocks, causing their own chemistry to change and, as a result, dissolved constituents may precipitate. Various minerals may crystallise within the fractures to give mineral veins. The composition of these veins depends on that of the fluid and on changes to the physical and chemical conditions taking place. The composition of the fluid depends partly on the nature of the rock from which it derived its soluble constituents or, in the case of aqueous fluids derived from magmas, on the composition of the magma. As fluids pass along fractures, minerals are deposited on the surfaces of the fracture to form a vein. Over time, with changing conditions or changing fluid composition, different minerals may be deposited in sequence on top of earlier minerals to produce mineral zonation from the margins inwards to the centre of the vein.

(b)

Figure 6.13 (a) Coarsely crystalline pegmatite vein containing quartz, potassium feldspar and long black crystals of tourmaline (a boron-rich mineral); (b) sugary-textured aplite vein (maximum width of vein is 10 cm).

The most common hydrothermal veins contain either quartz or calcite. The silica from which quartz veins are formed is released when silicate minerals break down during both metamorphism and hydrothermal alteration; it may also be derived by slight dissolution of quartz in permeable sedimentary rocks. Calcite veins are often formed following solution of limestone and may occur within the limestone itself and in adjacent rocks.

Question 6.3

If you were in the field, how would you decide whether the translucent, crystalline mineral in a vein was quartz or calcite?

Hydrothermal veins may also contain economically important **ore minerals** from which metals may be derived, such as galena (PbS), an ore mineral of lead; sphalerite (ZnS), an ore mineral of zinc; chalcopyrite ($CuFeS_2$), an ore mineral of copper; cassiterite (SnO_2), an ore mineral of tin; and molybdenite (MoS_2), an ore mineral of molybdenum (examples in Figure 6.14 and the Digital Kit). Economic deposits are generally much less common than simple quartz or calcite veining, although some parts of the UK, such as the North Pennines (for Pb–Cu–Zn) and southwest England (for Cu–Sn) were important as orefields for many centuries. Today, hydrothermal ores are of major economic importance to the metals mining industry in Australia, Canada, China and Brazil among many other countries.

(a) (b)

Figure 6.14 Hydrothermal mineral deposits: (a) an example of a banded vein (25 cm) from North Wales, with zones of white quartz, reddish-brown sphalerite, dark-grey galena and creamy dolomite; (b) molybdenite disseminated in a quartz vein (4 cm) from Glen Gairn, Scotland.

6.6 Chemical composition of igneous rocks

So far, you have considered the importance of magma composition only in terms of the minerals produced when it cools and crystallises. However, the mineral assemblage in a rock is a reflection of its chemical composition. Thus gabbro, dolerite and basalt consist essentially of the same minerals and have essentially the same chemical composition. Likewise, diorite, microdiorite and andesite have the same mineral and chemical composition; and granite, microgranite and rhyolite are also mineralogically and chemically the same.

The bulk chemical composition of a rock is usually found by crushing it to fine powder, which is then analysed to determine the abundance of elements present. Most elements present are contributed by more than one mineral. For example, granite consists of the following minerals:

- quartz, SiO_2
- alkali feldspar, $(K,Na)AlSi_3O_8$
- plagioclase feldspar, $NaAlSi_3O_8$–$CaAl_2Si_2O_8$
- biotite mica, $K(Mg,Fe)_3AlSi_3O_{10}(OH)_2$ with or without muscovite mica, $KAl_3Si_3O_{10}(OH)_2$

All these minerals contribute O and Si to the total analysis. In addition, the alkali feldspar contributes K, Na and Al, whereas plagioclase feldspar contributes Na, Ca and Al. Biotite contributes Mg and Fe, as well as K and Al.

Two examples of chemical analyses of igneous rocks are given in Table 6.3. These analyses can be used to illustrate some general principles about the chemical composition of rocks. Analyses of the major chemical components of rocks are normally presented as element oxides. This is a convention arising from the fact that oxygen is the dominant element in silicate rocks and minerals, and mineral formulae can usually be written as element oxides, for example alkali feldspar as $(K_2O,Na_2O).Al_2O_3.6SiO_2$. Also the total of all the constituents with appropriate amounts of oxygen accounted for should amount to about 100%.

Table 6.3 Representative chemical compositions[a] of a typical gabbro and granite. Note that iron can occur in different oxidation states, as Fe^{2+} or Fe^{3+}, which is why it is listed as two different oxides.

Oxide	Wt % oxide in gabbro	Wt % oxide in granite
SiO_2	48	70
TiO_2	2.5	0.5
Al_2O_3	15	15
Fe_2O_3	3	1
FeO	8	2
MgO	10	1
CaO	10	2.5
Na_2O	2	4
K_2O	1	3
H_2O	0.5	1

[a] The compositions are given as the percentages by weight (equivalent to mass) of the oxides. The order of listing is by convention.

It is important to realise, however, that the use of oxides in this way does not in any way imply the presence of equivalent oxide minerals in the rock. For example, although the gabbro in Table 6.3 contains 48 wt % SiO_2 there is unlikely to be any quartz or other silica mineral (whose formula would also be SiO_2) in the rock because in gabbroic magma all the available SiO_2 is combined with other elements to form Ca-rich plagioclase, pyroxene and olivine. In the granite, however, there is enough SiO_2 left over after allocation to feldspars and micas for it to be present as quartz. In general, rocks whose chemical analyses have less than about 60–65 wt % SiO_2 are *unlikely* to contain significant amounts of quartz, whereas those that have more than 60–65 wt % SiO_2 are *most* likely to contain quartz.

Although Si may occur as its oxide, quartz (SiO_2), it is important to realise that, in igneous rocks, the elements Mg, Ca, Na and K *never* occur as oxide minerals, and only some (but not most) of the Fe and Ti (and Al rarely) may occur as oxide accessory minerals.

Question 6.4

(a) According to Table 6.3, which oxide components are considerably more abundant in gabbro than granite?
(b) Which minerals are likely to account for the higher CaO content in gabbro than in granite?
(c) Which minerals are likely to account for the higher Fe_2O_3, FeO and MgO content in gabbro than in granite?

Silicate minerals that contain little or no iron or magnesium are called **felsic minerals**. The most common examples are quartz, feldspar and muscovite mica. Clearly, the higher the SiO_2 content of an igneous rock, the greater the proportion of these minerals, so rocks such as granite may be called **felsic rocks**. These rocks tend to be light in colour on account of their light-coloured constituent minerals. Silicate minerals that contain high proportions of iron and/or magnesium are called **mafic minerals** (also ferromagnesian minerals): the most common examples are olivine (($Mg,Fe)_2SiO_4$) and pyroxene ($(Mg,Fe,Ca)Si_2O_6$) (together with amphibole and biotite mica). Rocks with a lower SiO_2 content, such as gabbro, have a higher proportion of these minerals and are called **mafic rocks**. These rocks tend to be dark coloured on account of the dark colouring of most mafic minerals. Rocks such as diorite, and its volcanic equivalent, andesite, have a SiO_2 content intermediate between that of granite and gabbro, and are known as **intermediate rocks**. Another group of rocks, including peridotite, which contain even less SiO_2 than the mafic rocks, are called **ultramafic rocks**. In this classification, summarised in Table 6.4, it is important to remember that the rock types are defined in terms of their SiO_2 content and *not* on the amount of quartz present, although this can often be a useful visual clue.

Table 6.4 Classification of igneous rocks by SiO_2 content and typical mineral composition.

Wt % SiO_2	Type and examples	Typical mineral composition of crystalline rocks*
<45	ultramafic, e.g. peridotite	*no quartz*; dominantly mafic minerals; Ca-rich plagioclase in minor amounts or absent
45–52	mafic, e.g. gabbro, basalt	*no quartz*; rich in mafic minerals and Ca-rich plagioclase
52–66	intermediate, e.g. diorite, andesite	*up to 20% quartz*; significant proportions of both felsic and mafic minerals; plagioclase contains roughly equal proportions of Ca and Na
>66	felsic, e.g. granite, rhyolite	*more than 20% quartz*; feldspars include both K-rich orthoclase or microcline and Na-rich plagioclase; mafic minerals less than 25%

*Volcanic rocks may contain glass: these observations apply only to fully crystalline rocks.

The relationship between the content of the chemical component, SiO_2, as recorded in chemical analyses of different kinds of igneous rock and the relative proportions of the minerals commonly present, is summarised in an idealised way in Figure 6.15. The mineral proportions are approximate, but provide a useful way of representing the variation in mineral content for the main kinds of fully crystallised (excluding glassy) igneous rocks.

Figure 6.15 emphasises the point that ultramafic and mafic rocks with low SiO_2 contents contain a high proportion of mafic minerals, whereas felsic rocks with high SiO_2 contents contain mainly felsic minerals. This applies regardless of grain size across the spectrum of rock compositions. Note that few igneous rocks (apart from some pegmatites and aplites) contain more than 75 wt % SiO_2 (Figure 6.15).

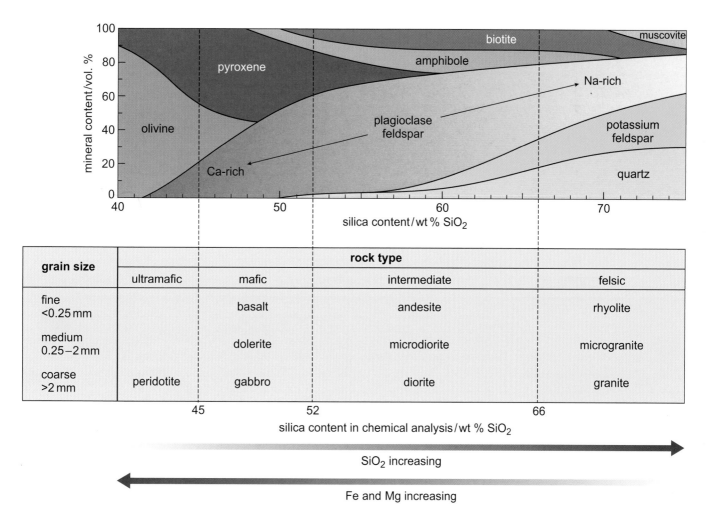

Figure 6.15 Diagram showing the approximate mineral and silica contents of a range of crystalline igneous rocks. Mafic minerals are olivine, pyroxene, amphibole and biotite; felsic minerals are quartz, feldspar and muscovite.

Question 6.5

A coarse-grained igneous rock has the chemical composition given in Table 6.5.

(a) Is it a felsic, intermediate or mafic rock (Table 6.4)?

(b) Suggest what minerals may be present and, from Figure 6.15, the approximate volume percentage of each mineral.

(c) What name could be given to the rock?

Table 6.5 The chemical composition of a coarse-grained igneous rock, for use in Question 6.5.

Oxide	Wt % oxide
SiO_2	55
Al_2O_3	18
$FeO + Fe_2O_3 + MgO$	13
CaO	8
$Na_2O + K_2O$	5
H_2O	1

6.7   Summary of Chapter 6

1   Most igneous rocks are formed when magma cools and crystallises, either on the Earth's surface as extrusive rocks, or beneath it, as intrusive rocks.

2   Rapid cooling of magma usually produces a fine-grained rock, which may even be glassy, whereas slow cooling usually gives a coarse-grained rock.

3   Crystals in an igneous rock form as a result of crystallisation around nucleation centres in the magma.

4   Phenocrysts in a rock often indicate crystallisation in two stages involving slow cooling at first, followed by more rapid cooling.

5   The fundamental control on the mineral composition of an igneous rock is the chemical composition of the magma from which it has crystallised; different mineral associations characterise particular types of igneous rock.

6   Rocks with similar mineralogy and chemical composition, but different grain size, are derived from the same type of magma but have different cooling histories.

7   Intrusive rocks are formed by the cooling of magma beneath the Earth's surface. They tend to be coarse grained, particularly plutonic rocks found as large intrusive bodies (plutons) that crystallised at considerable depths.

8   Extrusive (volcanic) rocks are formed from magma that has erupted at the Earth's surface. They tend to be fine grained as a result of rapid cooling.

9   Pyroclastic rocks are the result of explosive eruptions involving fragmentation of solidifying magma.

10 Pegmatites are igneous rocks that crystallise from magma rich in volatiles, especially water. Aplites form by rapid crystallisation of a magma when volatile constituents are suddenly lost to an escaping aqueous fluid.

11 Hydrothermal veins are sheets of minerals that have been deposited in fractures from hot aqueous solutions sometimes derived from associated igneous activity.

12 The proportions of the different element oxides in a chemical analysis reflect the relative proportions of the various minerals in the rock.

13 Igneous rocks may be classified as ultramafic, mafic, intermediate or felsic according to their SiO_2 content.

6.8   Objectives for Chapter 6

Now you have completed this chapter, you should be able to:

6.1 Identify the grain size and textures of fine-grained, medium-grained, coarse-grained, porphyritic and glassy igneous rocks, and thereby interpret the relative rate of cooling of magmas from which they formed.

6.2 Recognise the common mineral associations found in igneous rocks.

6.3 Give names to common igneous rocks on the basis of their grain size and mineral content.

6.4 Explain in general terms how the mineralogy of an igneous rock relates to its overall chemical composition.

6.5 Classify an igneous rock as ultramafic, mafic, intermediate or felsic on the basis of its SiO_2 content.

Now try the following questions to test your understanding of Chapter 6.

Question 6.6

Considering the examples of granite and porphyritic rhyolite in the Home Kit (also the Digital Kit and Virtual Microscope), explain how the principal difference between these two rocks could lie in their rates of cooling.

Question 6.7

A medium-grained igneous rock contains minerals in the proportions given in Table 6.6.

Table 6.6   The mineral composition of an igneous rock, for use in Question 6.7.

Mineral	Vol. %
quartz	6
potassium feldspar	6
plagioclase feldspar	62
biotite mica	12
amphibole	14

(a) Using information from Figure 6.15, what name would you give to this rock?

(b) What would be the approximate SiO_2 content of a rock with this mineralogy?

(c) What names would you give to the volcanic and plutonic equivalents of this rock?

Question 6.8

A fine-grained igneous rock has the chemical composition given in Table 6.7.

(a) Use Table 6.4 and Figure 6.15 to decide whether the rock is ultramafic, mafic, intermediate or felsic.

(b) What minerals are likely to be present and in approximately what proportions?

(c) What is the name of the rock?

Table 6.7 The chemical composition of an igneous rock, for use in Question 6.8.

Oxide	Wt % oxide
SiO_2	48
Al_2O_3	17
$FeO + Fe_2O_3 + MgO$	19
CaO	12
$Na_2O + K_2O$	3
H_2O	1

Question 6.9

Explain why an igneous rock containing 43 wt % SiO_2 and 44 wt % $FeO + Fe_2O_3 + MgO$ in its chemical analysis is likely to contain a high proportion of mafic minerals.

Question 6.10

Give two reasons why you would classify granite as a felsic rock.

Chapter 7   Sedimentary rocks

The material that forms most sedimentary rocks is derived by the weathering and erosion of pre-existing rocks of any kind and accumulates as a result of diverse physical, chemical and biological processes. Many sedimentary rocks are made up of mineral grains or rock fragments (also called **clasts**) that have been transported by water, wind or ice. They are deposited as sediments in layers and become consolidated during burial to form sedimentary rocks. Such rocks generally have a fragmental texture (Section 5.1) and are known as **clastic** rocks. Some sedimentary rocks originate from the materials that are dissolved during weathering and later precipitated from freshwater or seawater by purely chemical processes or through biological activities, especially shell secretion. Such rocks may accumulate by crystallisation *in situ* or may be deposited as fragments following transportation, and have crystalline or fragmental textures, respectively.

Physical weathering breaks up rock *in situ* by processes such as the freeze–thaw action of frost and ice, producing smaller fragments of rock and mineral grains. **Erosion**, in contrast, involves the breakup and removal of material by the dynamic action of water, wind or ice. Rocks may also be eroded by the abrasive action of transported grains, which wear away themselves at the same time. **Chemical weathering** involves the breakdown of minerals by chemical reaction as shown, for example, in Equation 7.1.

$$2KAlSi_3O_8(s) + 2H^+(aq) + H_2O(l) = Al_2Si_2O_5(OH)_4(s) + 2K^+(aq) + 4SiO_2(aq)$$
$$\text{potassium} \qquad\qquad\qquad\qquad \text{kaolinite}$$
$$\text{feldspar}$$
$$(7.1)$$

Dissolution by acidic solutions (e.g. rainwater and humic acids in soils) produces insoluble products, such as clay minerals (Section 4.5.2) and iron oxides, and soluble components that are removed in solution. Quartz is resistant to chemical weathering, and often remains after other minerals in a rock have been broken down. Insoluble aluminium and iron oxides and hydroxides may also remain after weathering, but soluble products, such as Na^+, Ca^{2+}, K^+ and Mg^{2+} ions, can be removed in solution by surface runoff or water percolating through the ground. These processes and their products are summarised in Figure 7.1.

Consolidation of sediments to form sedimentary rocks, a process known as **lithification**, may occur in several ways. In permeable rocks, percolating water can dissolve mineral grains such as calcite or even quartz and may, when conditions change, recrystallise the same minerals as a cement, which binds together the remaining grains by **cementation**, making a solid rock. As sediments accumulate to progressively greater thicknesses, buried layers become compressed by the weight of the overlying sediments. With **compaction**, grains become more tightly packed, the spaces (or pores) between them become greatly reduced, and much of the water present is squeezed out.

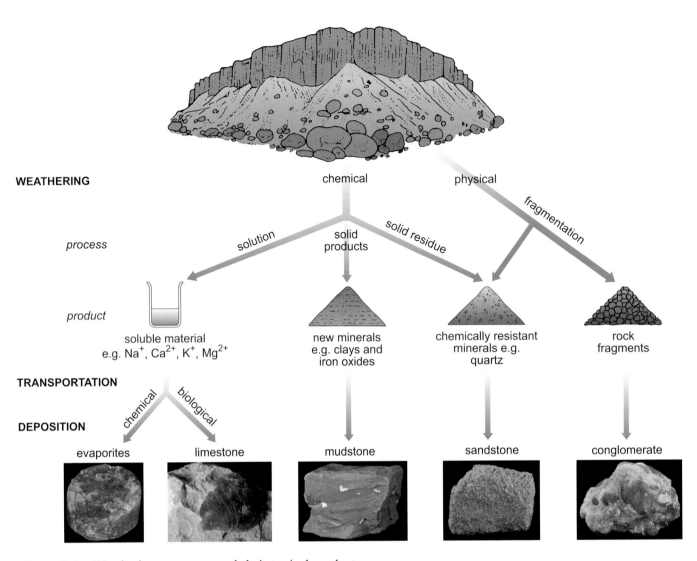

WEATHERING

chemical   physical

fragmentation

process

solution   solid products   solid residue

product

soluble material
e.g. Na^+, Ca^{2+}, K^+, Mg^{2+}

new minerals
e.g. clays and
iron oxides

chemically resistant
minerals e.g.
quartz

rock
fragments

TRANSPORTATION

chemical   biological

DEPOSITION

evaporites   limestone   mudstone   sandstone   conglomerate

Figure 7.1   Weathering processes and their typical products.

Figure 7.2   Bedded sedimentary rocks exposed
in a cliff face, South Wales.

The combination of factors involved in weathering, erosion, transportation, deposition and consolidation determines the nature of the resulting sedimentary rock. Because sediments are usually deposited in layers, visible bedding in rocks exposed in road cuttings and cliffs is often the first clue in the field that rocks *may* be sedimentary (Figure 7.2).

■   Would you expect all rocks that appear to be deposited in layers to be sedimentary rocks?

☐   No, some volcanic rocks, notably basaltic lava flows and pyroclastic deposits, are also layered, and metamorphic rocks, formed from sedimentary rocks, may retain their original sedimentary layering.

7.1 Siliciclastic rocks

The solid products of weathering are removed by erosion in streams and rivers, by glaciers or the wind, and are transported, often over considerable distances. During transportation, rock and mineral fragments are often broken down further, their survival depending on properties such as hardness, durability and chemical stability. Chemically and physically stable grains of rock or minerals gradually become more rounded and less angular as they are abraded, for example against the riverbed and other grains. Such deposits, when derived from silicate rocks and usually composed of quartz and/or clay minerals and/or silicate-rich rock fragments, are described as **siliciclastic**.

The ease with which a mineral grain may be transported or deposited by water or wind depends on its shape, size and density. In any particular transporting medium, and for grains of equal density, there is a limit to the grain size that can be transported at a given flow speed; anything larger would be deposited. A higher rate of flow is required initially for grains to be picked up and transported. At high flow rates, a wide range of grain sizes, including larger fragments, can be transported. As the current slackens, the coarsest, densest grains are deposited first; the finest, lightest grains are deposited last. This process is known as **sorting**.

Both chemical decomposition and physical sorting can play a role in separating out mineral grains of contrasting size, density and chemical composition. The result of these processes may eventually be a uniform deposit composed entirely of sand grains or of clay particles, as illustrated in Figure 7.1.

One important way in which siliciclastic rocks (and most other sedimentary rocks) may be classified is based on their grain size. Grain size can be judged to a good approximation using a hand lens and a grain size scale. Figure 7.3 shows how grains of common materials (salt and granulated sugar) may be classified by laying grains of each onto a piece of black paper and comparing individual grains with the grain size scale.

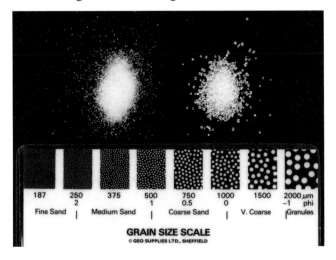

Figure 7.3 Use of a grain size scale to show the difference in the size of grains of salt (left) and granulated sugar (right).

■ Using the grain size scale in Figure 7.3, what is the grain size classification of the salt and the sugar?

☐ The salt grains are equivalent to a medium-grained sand (~375 μm) and the granulated sugar grains match a coarse-grained sand (~750 μm).

In some sediments the grains are all about the same size, whereas others contain a wide range of grain sizes. The former are said to be **well sorted** by size (Figure 7.4a). These grains have either been sorted by current activity during transportation and deposition, or derived from a source already comprising evenly sized grains. By contrast, a sediment that contains a variety of grain sizes is **poorly sorted** (Figure 7.4b). This is indicative of a wide range of materials being deposited at once, such as from a melting ice sheet or when a fast-flowing current carrying a range of grain sizes slows abruptly. In such deposits, the spaces between large grains are usually occupied by finer-grained **matrix** material.

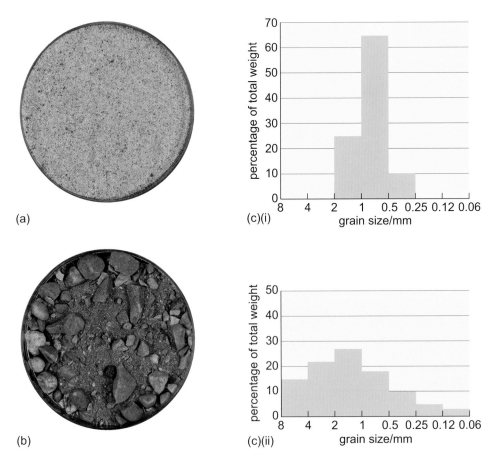

(a)

(b)

(c)(i)

(c)(ii)

Figure 7.4 Sediment with: (a) a narrow range of grain sizes (well sorted); (b) a wide range of grain sizes (poorly sorted). (The dishes are 8 cm in diameter.) (c) Grain size histograms (i) and (ii) of sediments similar to those shown in (a) and (b).

In a sedimentary rock, the volumetrically most significant grains determine its grain size classification. The size classification of siliciclastic sediments and sedimentary rocks is outlined in Figure 7.5. When the volumetrically most abundant grains are of sand size (i.e. from 62.5 µm to 2 mm), though not necessarily composed of quartz, the rock is a **sandstone**. Coarser-grained sediments may vary in size from granules to boulders. On compaction and cementation, the rock is known as a **conglomerate** if the clasts are rounded, or a **breccia** if the clasts are angular.

Finer-grained sediments may be either silt (from 4 µm to 62.5 µm) from which **siltstone** is derived, or clay (<4 µm), giving a **claystone**. The term **mudstone** encompasses both siltstones and claystones as well as rocks that contain a mixture of both clay- and silt-sized particles. If a mudstone splits easily into thin layers parallel to bedding (i.e. is fissile) it is known as **shale**.

Grain size (most volumetrically abundant grains)[a]	Sediment name	Sedimentary rock name
>256 mm	boulders	
64–256 mm	cobbles	conglomerate (rounded fragments) or breccia (angular fragments)
4–64 mm	pebbles (gravel)	
2–4 mm	granules	
62.5 µm–2 mm	sand	sandstone
4–62.5 µm	silt (mud)	siltstone
<4 µm	clay[b]	claystone (mudstone (shale)[c])

Figure 7.5 Grain size scale for siliciclastic rocks. Geologists sometimes *informally* subdivide sediments and sedimentary rocks into three grain size divisions: 'fine-grained deposits' are clay and silt grade (i.e. mud/mudstone); 'medium-grained deposits' are sand grade; and any deposits coarser than sand grade are often called 'coarse-grained deposits'. Note that the volumetrically most significant grains in a sedimentary rock determine its classification.
[a] µm = micrometre = 10^{-6} m. The grain size classification is divided at arbitrary, but not random, sizes: 256 mm is 2^8 mm, 64 mm is 2^6 mm, 62.5 µm is $\frac{1}{2^4}$ mm, and 4 µm is almost exactly $\frac{1}{2^8}$ mm. [b] Clay can have two meanings: it may refer to material with a *grain size* of less than 4 µm or to a certain type of sheet silicate mineral (i.e. clay minerals, Section 4.5.2). However, most clay-sized particles in sedimentary rocks are, in fact, clay minerals. [c] Shale, if fissile.

Activity 7.1 Grain size in sedimentary rocks

In this activity, you will investigate the grain size variation in a range of sedimentary rocks.

The morphology or shape of sedimentary grains may be described in terms of their sphericity and roundness:

- **sphericity** is a measure of how closely the shape of a grain approaches that of a sphere

- **roundness** is concerned with the curvature of the surface of the grain.

Six categories, from very angular to well rounded, are illustrated in Figure 7.6. Note that a grain may be well rounded but not necessarily have a high sphericity, as for example if the grain is shaped more like an ellipsoid. Well-rounded grains are often indicative of transportation and deposition by wind action. Grains hitting each other in air lack the cushioning effect that water provides, and the impacts knock off surface irregularities.

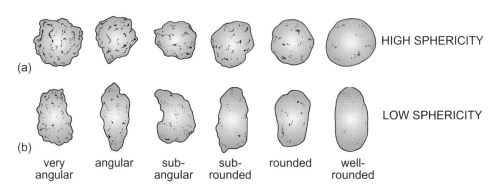

Figure 7.6 The morphology of sedimentary grains. For each category of roundness, grains of low and high sphericity are shown.

The **surface texture** of sedimentary grains can often give a clue as to their origin and to the form of transportation. Water-borne grains, as found in rivers and on beaches (Figure 7.7a), are usually angular with glassy surfaces (like broken window or bottle glass), whereas wind-blown grains, as found in deserts (Figure 7.7b), are usually dull and frosted (like the obscured glass used for bathroom windows) from repeated impacts that create tiny pits.

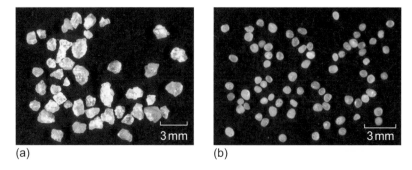

Figure 7.7 (a) Angular and glassy sedimentary grains from a beach sand. (b) Rounded and frosted sedimentary grains from a desert sand.

The arrangement of sedimentary grains may display a particular **fabric**, relating to the orientation, packing and the nature of contacts between individual grains. If deposited in a current, elongate clasts may tend to be aligned preferentially in a particular orientation. **Packing** describes the way in which sedimentary grains are stacked: grains of equal size will tend to be loosely packed, whereas grains of different sizes will be more closely packed, with smaller grains occupying the spaces between larger grains. As illustrated in Figure 7.8, if the larger grains:

- are in contact with each other, the fabric is described as **grain supported** (like cherries in a jar)
- are not in contact but seem to 'float' in finer matrix material, then the fabric is described as **matrix supported** (like cherries in a cake).

Some siliciclastic rocks contain a limited range of grain types, whereas in others there is a variety. A **wacke** is a sandstone that contains more than 15% of fine-grained matrix. An **arkose** (RS 18) is a sandstone rich in feldspar (usually potassium feldspar), often with some quartz and a few small rock fragments. The term is normally used for rocks containing more than 25% feldspar. Sandstones are termed **compositionally mature** when they consist mainly of quartz and are the end-products of the weathering process in which most physically and chemically unstable grains have been removed. Sandstones containing rock fragments and chemically less-durable minerals, such as feldspars, are **compositionally immature**.

Activity 7.2 Grain types in sedimentary rocks

In this activity, you will use the Virtual Microscope to identify the mineral constituents of a range of sandstones.

7.2 Carbonate rocks

Carbonate rocks, especially **limestones**, are the most widespread group of sedimentary rocks that are not of silicate composition. Limestones are usually made of calcium carbonate ($CaCO_3$) in the form of calcite, but some are composed of dolomite ($CaMg(CO_3)_2$). Most limestones are of biological origin, formed by the extraction of calcium carbonate from seawater by organisms to make their shells and skeletons. Some organisms are microscopic and float in the surface waters of seas and oceans; others, such as clams, mussels, sea urchins and corals, live on the sea floor. The skeletal remains of these organisms accumulate on the sea floor and become consolidated (often cemented) to form limestones. As noted in Section 4.7.1, organic precipitation of calcium carbonate is sometimes as the aragonite polymorph, which over time transforms into calcite.

Because they are composed of calcium carbonate, most limestones will 'fizz' with dilute (5–10%) hydrochloric acid (HCl) (Section 4.7.1). This is a useful diagnostic test for limestone in hand specimen and in the field. However, a limestone that consists of dolomite rather than calcite will not usually react with the dilute acid unless the test is made on powdered rock.

Many limestones can easily be cut and quarried, making them well-suited for use as building stones. When they are sufficiently homogeneous to be cut or split equally easily in any direction, they are known as **freestones**. However, limestones are very susceptible to chemical weathering because they dissolve

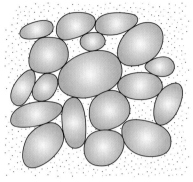

(a) grain-supported fabric

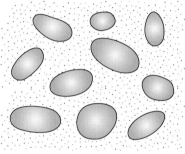

(b) matrix-supported fabric

Figure 7.8 (a) Grain-supported fabric. (b) Matrix-supported fabric.

in rainwater that is acidic owing to the presence in solution of atmospheric gases, such as carbon dioxide, and more especially to the gaseous pollutants sulfur dioxide (SO_2) and nitrogen oxides (NO_x). This effect is particularly noticeable on limestone carvings and statues (Figure 7.9a). The dissolution of carbonates by water and dissolved carbon dioxide is described by Equation 7.2.

$$CaCO_3(s) + H_2O(l) + CO_2(aq) = Ca^{2+}(aq) + 2HCO_3^-(aq) \qquad (7.2)$$

Exposed limestone surfaces in the landscape have been etched by acidic solutions (especially by organic acids developed in soils) along regular arrangements of fractures or joints to give a characteristic limestone 'pavement' (Figure 7.9b). In extreme cases, this may give rise to extensive underground networks of potholes and caves, such as found at Cheddar Gorge in Somerset and the Caves of Drach in Majorca.

(a)

(b)

Figure 7.9 (a) Heavily corroded ornamental carvings. (b) Limestone pavement at The Burren, Ireland.

The textures of limestones are extremely variable. Many limestones are made up of shell fragments or skeletal remains, which are collectively termed **bioclasts** (e.g. Figure 7.10a).

Activity 7.3 Bioclasts in limestones

This activity focuses on the nature of the fragmental material in limestones.

A particular type of clast often found in limestones is the result of direct precipitation of calcium carbonate from seawater. Small rounded grains (called **ooids**) are developed in warm, agitated shallow waters, especially in tidal

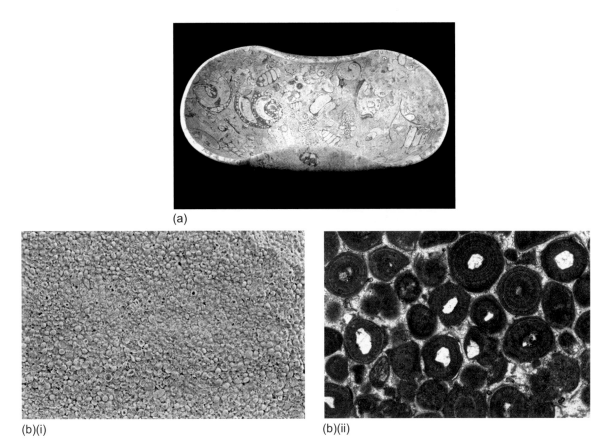

(a)

(b)(i)

(b)(ii)

Figure 7.10 (a) Carved bowl made of bioclastic limestone (25 cm). (b)(i) Oolitic texture in hand specimen (field of view 2 cm) and (ii) ooids in thin section in plane-polarised light (field of view 3 mm) (see also RS 22 and the Digital Kit).

shallows, and accumulate to form a sediment that has a texture with the appearance of fish roe, known as **oolitic** texture (Figure 7.10b). When consolidated this becomes oolitic limestone, which has a distinctive appearance and is easily recognised in hand specimen (RS 22 and Digital Kit). Well-cemented examples are often used as freestones, much prized for building and ornamental work.

Activity 7.4 Oolitic limestone

This activity investigates the constituents of oolitic limestone.

Another type of limestone, familiar to many in northwest Europe, is **chalk** (RS 8 and the Digital Kit), which is well exposed along parts of England's southern and eastern coasts (e.g. the White Cliffs of Dover, and Flamborough Head, Figure 7.11a). It is a very fine-grained limestone made from the minute skeletal plates (**coccoliths**) of untold numbers of tiny marine algae (Figure 7.11b (i) and (ii)). On death, these coccoliths accumulated as a carbonate-rich mud on the sea floor and were compacted during burial.

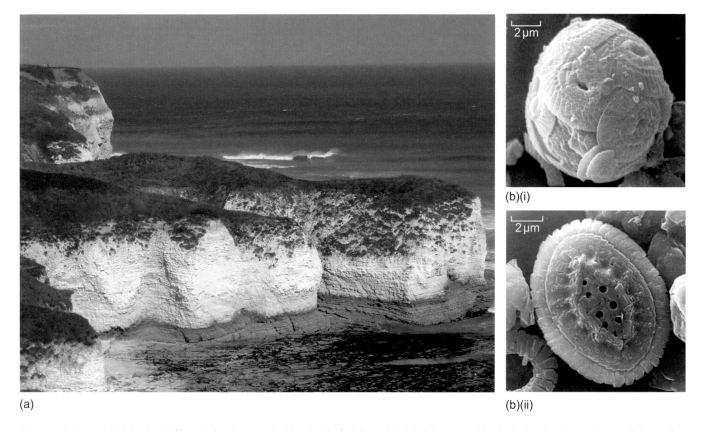

(a)

(b)(i)

(b)(ii)

Figure 7.11 (a) Chalk cliffs at Flamborough Head, Yorkshire. (b) Highly magnified skeletal plates (coccoliths) of tiny marine algae in chalk: (i) complete cell coating of coccolith plates; (ii) isolated coccolith from a different species.

7.3   Other sedimentary deposits

7.3.1   Evaporites

During the chemical weathering of rocks, some minerals break down and the soluble products are transported in solution and accumulate in seas or, sometimes, in inland lakes. With evaporation from confined lakes or seas, the concentrations of soluble constituents increase to produce saline solutions. However, a given volume of solution can hold only a certain amount of dissolved material, so if evaporation continues, the concentration of dissolved constituents eventually reaches a saturation limit, beyond which evaporite minerals crystallise out. This process is analogous to the commercial extraction of common salt (NaCl) from seawater in artificial ponds (solars) in many hot climates where evaporation rates are high. Similar processes have occurred naturally under hot, dry conditions in shallow coastal basins and mudflats many times in the geological past, leaving large salt deposits, many of which are economically important. Sedimentary deposits formed in this way are known as **evaporites**. In Britain, major evaporite deposits occur underground in Cheshire and Cleveland, as part of the Permian-age Zechstein Basin that extends across much of central northern Europe into Russia. These deposits form an important economic resource.

Two economically important evaporite minerals are: **rock salt** (Figure 7.12a), composed of the mineral halite (NaCl) (Figure 2.13c), used by the chemicals industry and for salting roads in winter; and gypsum ($CaSO_4.2H_2O$; Figure 7.12b), used to make plaster for the building industry. Evaporites are very susceptible to dissolution and are not often found at the surface, except in dry climates.

7.3.2 Chert

Chemically or biologically precipitated rocks formed of microcrystalline quartz, known as **chert**, and composed only of silica, are often found in association with limestones. Possibly the best known are the nodular lumps of chert, known as **flint** (Figure 7.13a), found within the chalk deposits of southern and eastern England, and often used in the region as ornamental building materials (Figure 7.13b). These cherts are secondary in origin – they have replaced part of the host rock after its deposition, having been precipitated from solutions derived from the silica-rich skeletons of sponges and marine plankton. Chert may also occur in bedded form as an accumulation of silica-rich skeletal material, the remains of planktonic organisms. These siliceous rocks are extremely fine grained (microcrystalline) and individual grains cannot be distinguished, even with the microscope. Like glass, they often break with sharp, conchoidal fracture surfaces, which were useful to many primitive cultures in the manufacture of axes, spears and arrows.

(a)

(b)

Figure 7.12 Examples of evaporite minerals: (a) rock salt (halite) (11 cm), (b) fibrous gypsum (2 cm). (See MS V and the Digital Kit.)

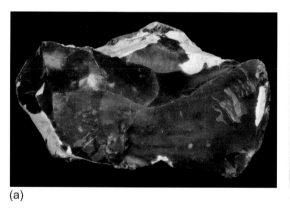

(a)

(b)

Figure 7.13 (a) Flint nodule (7.5 cm) showing conchoidal fracture surfaces (see also MS III and the Digital Kit). (b) Flint used as a building stone.

Lumps such as flint that have formed by precipitation *in situ* within a rock are often described as **nodules** or **concretions**. Many nodules consist of carbonate minerals; others may include phosphatic or iron minerals. The conditions required for such nodules to grow are complex, but nodules often form around a particular object, such as a decaying organism that provides suitable chemical conditions.

■ What is the difference between nodules and pebbles?

☐ Pebbles are clasts and arrive in place at the time of deposition of a sediment, whereas nodules grow *after* deposition during burial.

7.3.3 Carbonaceous deposits

The soft parts of organisms normally decay after death, primarily due to oxidation and bacterial action, and their constituents, mainly carbon and hydrogen, are released and recycled. However, in suitable settings such as in swamps and bogs or on stagnant sea floors and lake bottoms, organic residues may be preserved within sediments.

In swamps and bogs, where the water is stagnant and where organic, carbon-rich matter – particularly plant material – accumulates faster than it decays, **peat** can form. If it is then deeply buried and compressed, it eventually forms **coal** (Figure 7.14). The quality (or **rank**) of coal varies depending on the burial history of the deposit and the extent to which volatiles have been driven off. Anthracite (highest rank) contains less than 10% volatiles; bituminous coal, with typically from 10 to 35% volatiles, produces coke on roasting which is used in the iron and steel industry. Coals with high volatile content (>30%) burn easily and are preferred for fuelling power stations. Coal has long been mined as a fuel and dominated energy supplies from the beginning of the Industrial Revolution to the mid-20th century. In Britain, the main deposits are bituminous coals in rocks of Carboniferous age, which extend beneath the North Sea into Germany and Poland. Important deposits of low rank brown coals of Tertiary age occur in eastern Europe. Except for Australia, the most extensive coal deposits are in the Northern Hemisphere.

Organic matter, especially microscopic planktonic organisms preserved in sediments of seas with stagnant bottom waters, has the potential under suitable temperature and pressure conditions during burial to produce liquid and/or gaseous hydrocarbons, known as **petroleum**. Some, mainly gaseous petroleum, derives from buried coal deposits. Suitable geological conditions are also required for these hydrocarbons to migrate and for them to become trapped in reservoir rock formations to produce petroleum deposits that can be exploited. Although there are oil and gas reserves scattered around the world, by far the greatest concentration (60% of oil; 40% of gas) is in the Middle East, mainly around the Persian Gulf, with significant gas reserves also in Russia.

Figure 7.14 Coal sample (4 cm). Sedimentary layering is just visible.

7.4 Mineral associations in sedimentary rocks

As you have now discovered, the processes of weathering, erosion, transportation and chemical or biochemical precipitation, usually followed by burial and lithification, lead to the formation of sedimentary rocks that are often composed mainly of quartz, clay minerals or calcite. Under suitable conditions, therefore, virtually pure sandstones, mudstones or limestones are formed, respectively, from these constituents. Many sedimentary rocks, however, are mixtures of these minerals, as represented in the ternary diagram,

Figure 7.15, where each corner of the triangle represents 100% of one of the three constituents.

The names given to sedimentary rocks formed by various combinations of these minerals are also shown in this classification scheme. Rocks composed mainly of quartz and calcite lie along the left-hand edge of the triangle (Figure 7.15). The name given depends on the relative proportions of quartz and calcite present: from limestone, through sandy limestone and calcareous sandstone, to pure quartz sandstone. Similarly, a range of names, from quartz sandstone to mudstone, is given to rocks along the right-hand edge of the triangle, and from limestone to mudstone along the bottom edge (a calcareous mudstone or muddy limestone is commonly referred to as a **marl**).

The middle part of Figure 7.15 corresponds to sedimentary rocks that contain substantial amounts of all three constituents: quartz, calcite and clay minerals. Hence, a limestone containing significant amounts of both quartz and clay minerals could be called a sandy muddy limestone.

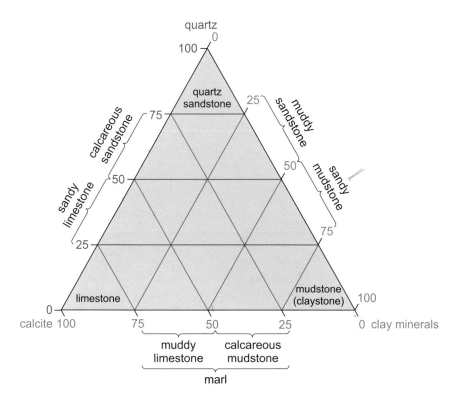

Figure 7.15 Ternary diagram showing the relative proportions of the principal mineral constituents of common sedimentary rocks. (Refer to Box 4.1 if you have problems reading this ternary diagram.)

Question 7.1

From Figure 7.15, what would you call a rock composed of the following constituents?

(a) 60% clay minerals and 40% quartz
(b) 60% quartz and 40% calcite
(c) 40% clay minerals and 60% calcite.

■ Figure 7.15 is somewhat simplified because, as you know from Section 7.1, a number of sedimentary rock constituents are not represented on it. What do you think they might be?

□ They could include rock fragments, feldspar, mica, iron oxides and organic matter.

You should recall from Section 7.1 that sandstones containing abundant feldspar are known as arkose. A sandstone containing a significant amount of mica could be described informally as a micaceous sandstone. Muscovite is more common than biotite in sedimentary rocks as biotite is more susceptible to weathering. Because of its flaky nature, mica is often blown away from sediments deposited by the wind. Its presence in a sedimentary rock, therefore, usually indicates deposition by water.

The mineral constituents of sedimentary rocks (particularly coarse-grained ones) are not only those of the fragmental debris or precipitated minerals in the sediment when it formed, but also mineral cements, especially calcite and quartz, which can be precipitated from percolating solutions.

■ Which kind of sedimentary rock might be more likely to contain a larger volume of mineral cement – a well-sorted coarse-grained sandstone or a muddy sandstone?

□ The well-sorted sandstone, because it would have more pore space between the sand grains that could be occupied by cement. In the muddy sandstone, mud-sized grains would occupy much of the space between the larger grains.

Percolating solutions often dissolve the mineral grains with which they come into contact and precipitate the cement in the pore spaces. Solutions commonly migrate from one type of sediment to another, so sandstones may have a calcareous (calcite) cement and calcareous organic debris could have a siliceous (quartz) cement. A well-sorted sediment that is not cemented undergoes compaction on burial, but a cemented sediment resists compaction. Well-sorted sediments with little if any cement are porous, and if the pores are connected they are permeable. Such poorly cemented rocks, including some sandstones and limestones, are extremely important to the petroleum industry as they can form petroleum reservoirs.

Lithification processes, including compaction and the precipitation of mineral cements such as these, may begin soon after a sediment is deposited, at ordinary atmospheric temperatures and pressures, and continue over long periods of time as temperatures and pressures progressively increase during burial. At temperatures above about 200 °C, and at much increased pressures, the minerals themselves may undergo change and a whole new group of rocks may form as a result of metamorphism. These are the subject of Chapter 8.

7.5 Summary of Chapter 7

1   Sedimentary rocks are the result of the accumulation of the products of physical weathering, chemical weathering, erosion and organic activity.

2   Siliciclastic rocks are formed from the solid products of physical and chemical weathering of silicate rocks.

3   Siliciclastic rocks are most often classified according to their grain size.

4   The morphology and surface texture of sedimentary grains developed during transportation provide clues as to their origin.

5   Carbonate rocks, commonly referred to as limestones, are largely composed of calcite, less commonly, of dolomite, and are usually the result of chemical or biochemical precipitation from seawater.

6   Evaporites are deposits formed as a result of evaporation of saline water in shallow basins and mudflats under hot, dry conditions.

7   Chert (including the variety, flint) is a form of microcrystalline quartz, often occurring in limestone as bedded layers and sometimes as irregular nodules formed as an *in situ* replacement of the rock.

8   In stagnant conditions of swamps and bogs, the accumulation of carbon-rich plant material can give rise to deposits of peat and coal, and subsequent heating of coal may lead to the formation of mainly gaseous petroleum. Most petroleum is produced by the accumulation of organic-rich marine deposits on the sea floor, followed by suitable conditions of burial.

9   The processes of weathering, erosion, transportation and chemical or biochemical precipitation tend to produce sedimentary rocks that are composed of quartz, clay minerals and calcite in various proportions; other components may include rock fragments, feldspar, mica (usually muscovite), iron oxides and organic matter.

7.6 Objectives for Chapter 7

Now you have completed this chapter, you should be able to:

7.1 Recognise the common groups of sedimentary rocks on the basis of their textures and mineralogical compositions.

7.2 Classify a sedimentary rock on the basis of its texture and mineralogy.

7.3 Describe the textural features of sedimentary grains.

7.4 Relate textures and mineral associations in common sedimentary rocks to their mode of origin.

7.5 Explain, in simple terms, weathering processes and their implications for the sediments produced.

Now try the following questions to test your understanding of Chapter 7.

Question 7.2

Considering the chemistry of the main minerals found in sedimentary rocks, to which minerals would you attribute the following?

(a) the high SiO_2 content of sandstone
(b) the high Al_2O_3 content of mudstone
(c) the high CaO and CO_2 content of limestone.

Question 7.3

Why do you think it might be that muscovite survives weathering better than biotite? (*Hint:* consider the temperatures at which they crystallise.)

Question 7.4

Which minerals would you expect to find in sediments derived from:
(a) quartz sandstone; (b) granite; (c) gabbro?

Chapter 8 Metamorphic rocks

Most rocks seen at the Earth's surface are solid, stable and appear to have an air of permanence about them. It is difficult to imagine them undergoing any change in form. However, when such rocks are subjected to the very high pressures and temperatures found deep within the Earth, especially at depths of more than about 10–12 km, they can develop new minerals and textures in the solid state (i.e. without melting). Such changes are the result of **metamorphism** and the new rocks formed are known as metamorphic rocks. Metamorphic rocks may be produced from igneous or sedimentary rocks, or even from pre-existing metamorphic rocks. In some instances, the metamorphic change may be minimal, and features of the original rock may still be apparent. In many cases, however, the rock changes so much that its original identity cannot be recognised without sophisticated laboratory investigations.

Question 8.1

What are the most likely causes of increased heat or pressure in rocks that might lead to metamorphism?

The simplest form of metamorphism results from heating when hot magma is intruded into colder rocks. This is known as **contact** (or **thermal**) **metamorphism** and is usually limited to the local area around the intrusion. Metamorphism on a larger scale occurs when rocks are deeply buried as a result of subsidence and thickening of the crust by deformation at zones of tectonic plate convergence and mountain building. With depth, the increase in pressure due to the weight of overlying rocks is accompanied by an increase in temperature according to the prevailing **geothermal gradient** (a measure of the rise in temperature with depth in the Earth). This large-scale metamorphism is known as **regional metamorphism**. As the name suggests, it generally affects vast volumes of rock. A less common and more localised form of metamorphism associated with movement and intense deformation along fault zones is known as **dynamic metamorphism**.

8.1 Contact metamorphism

When hot magma is intruded into colder rocks, they become 'baked' by heat dissipated from the intrusion. The extent of baking or contact metamorphism of the surrounding rocks, called **country rocks**, depends on the amount of magma providing the heat, and its temperature. The zone of contact metamorphism around an igneous intrusion is known as a **metamorphic aureole**. For a minor intrusion such as a dyke or sill, the zone of baking may only be centimetres or at most a few metres wide, but the aureole of a large pluton may be several kilometres wide.

Intense contact metamorphism (of sedimentary rocks, especially) produces a fine-grained, hard, splintery rock, known as **hornfels**, which is a purely textural rather than compositional term. A suitable analogy is the manufacture of pottery. Soft clay pots are transformed (metamorphosed) in kilns into hard, brittle objects by firing at temperatures of 1000 °C or more. This analogy illustrates three fundamental aspects of metamorphism:

- Changes usually occur in the solid state without melting (although some melting may occur under extreme conditions).

- There is usually no significant change in the overall chemical composition, although volatile constituents, such as water and gases, may be lost.

- The chemical elements that make up the original minerals (clay minerals in the 'pots' example) are redistributed into new minerals with crystal structures that are more stable under the new conditions.

Since contact metamorphism is the result of heat alone, it typically occurs in the absence of strong deformation. Any new minerals that form tend to grow in random orientations so that contact metamorphic rocks, such as hornfelses, break unevenly in random directions, as do pots fired in a kiln. Sometimes, a particular mineral grows larger than others, such as the andalusite in Figure 8.1. Some minerals may form more diffuse masses which give the rock a 'spotted' appearance.

Figure 8.1 Andalusite slate from the contact zone around the Skiddaw granite intrusion, Cumbria. The large grey or white prismatic crystals (12 mm) are due to growth of the mineral andalusite within a rock that was already a slate (and retains some of its slaty character) when it was further metamorphosed by the heat of the intruding granite.

8.2 Regional metamorphism

Regional metamorphic rocks are formed in zones of crustal thickening due to deformation associated with mountain building. New minerals form in response to increased pressure, as well as increased temperature, when rocks reside for long enough deep in the Earth's crust. Compressive stresses associated with tectonic movements and deformation cause any newly crystallising minerals with unequal dimensions to form more or less parallel to one another, oriented in response to the compression (Figure 8.2c–d). This applies particularly to minerals that typically form platy (flat) crystals (e.g. mica) or elongate prismatic crystals (e.g. amphibole) (Figure 8.2a–b).

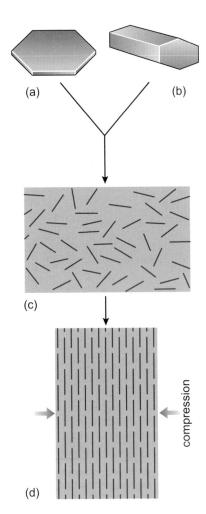

Figure 8.2 The development of mineral alignment in metamorphic rocks: (a) platy mica crystal; (b) prismatic amphibole crystal; (c) random distribution of mica or amphibole; (d) the alignment of platy or elongate crystals by compression.

The planar fabric produced by the alignment of platy minerals (e.g. micas and chlorite) is known as **foliation**; the directional alignment of the long axes of prismatic minerals (e.g. amphibole) is known as **lineation** (Figure 8.3).

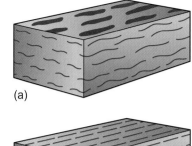

(a)

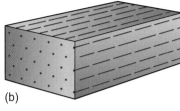

(b)

Activity 8.1   Foliation and lineation in regionally metamorphosed rocks

In this activity, you will use the Virtual Microscope to see mineral alignment that produces foliation and lineation.

Figure 8.3   Simplified diagrams to illustrate: (a) the alignment of platy minerals to produce a planar fabric or foliation; (b) the alignment of prismatic minerals to produce lineation. Most regionally metamorphosed rocks have a foliation; some have a lineation.

In regionally metamorphosed rocks, the degree of development of foliation and banding is used with grain size to describe the texture of the rock. In a general way, the degree of metamorphism to which a rock has been subjected is referred to as the **grade** of metamorphism: *low* grade at lower temperatures and pressures; *high* grade at higher temperatures and pressures. Under the lowest grades of metamorphism, in fine-grained rocks that had been mudstones or shales, very closely spaced, flat foliation planes are formed, to give a **slate** (Figure 8.4a). Slate has been an important building material, used for roofing, because it can be split easily along its foliation planes to form thin, rigid sheets. This property is known as cleavage or, more correctly, **slaty cleavage**, formed as a result of mineral alignment in fine-grained, low-grade metamorphic rocks. It is very different from the cleavage in minerals, which is due to planes of weakness in the crystal structure (Section 2.3.4).

(a)   (b)   (c)

(d)   (e)

Figure 8.4   Examples of metamorphic rocks: (a) slate (3.5 cm) (RS 2); (b) phyllite (5.5 cm) (RS 11); (c) schist (6 cm) (RS 26); (d) amphibolite (3.5 cm) (RS 16); (e) gneiss (5 cm) (RS 4).

As the temperature, pressure and duration of metamorphism increase, the crystals grow larger, the grain size increases, and foliation surfaces become more uneven and widely separated. Rocks with foliation surfaces that have a silky, but 'wrinkled' appearance, having undergone a slightly higher grade of metamorphism than slates, are known as **phyllites** (Figure 8.4b).

Slates and phyllites are produced only from fine-grained, clay-rich sedimentary rocks, such as shale or mudstone. If a basalt or a sandstone were to be metamorphosed under those same conditions, it would probably show very little sign of recrystallisation, any effect being barely visible to the naked eye. A coarse-grained sediment could not develop a good slaty cleavage.

With increasing metamorphic grade and continued growth of platy mica flakes, the foliation becomes even more undulating and is known as **schistosity**; the rocks are called **schists** (pronounced 'shist') (Figure 8.4c). Elongate, prismatic minerals, such as amphibole, may also form a schistosity, but when amphibole is predominant, the rock is usually called an **amphibolite** (Figure 8.4d). Apart from a few exceptions, metamorphic rock terminology is quite simple because it describes the texture of the rock, but textural variation is gradational, and some examples could equally well be called one or the other.

With further increase in grade of metamorphism, small-scale migration of chemical elements may cause felsic and mafic minerals to be segregated into distinct, alternating bands, known as **metamorphic banding**. The bands are not always sharply defined and may grade one into another. Such a medium- or coarse-grained, banded metamorphic rock is known as a **gneiss** (pronounced 'nice') (Figure 8.4e) (though some schists may also exhibit some mineral segregation).

Question 8.2

In Figure 8.4e, the mineral that makes up the darker bands is biotite. Describe how you would recognise this mineral in thin section.

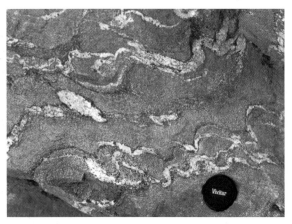

Figure 8.5 Example of migmatite (note lens cap for scale).

Gneisses can be formed from a variety of rocks, including igneous rocks, sandstones, siltstones and mudstones. Under extreme conditions of regional metamorphism, a schist or a gneiss may start to melt to form a 'mixed rock' known as a **migmatite** (Figure 8.5). In this rock, light-coloured felsic layers or patches represent crystallised molten material that has separated from the dark-coloured mafic layers or patches that represent unmelted, residual minerals. With further melting, the molten layers may coalesce and magma may be released, which, on cooling, will solidify to form a felsic igneous rock. Coarse-grained metamorphic rocks that have been subjected to extreme metamorphic conditions and have not melted, yet have lost their volatile constituents and as a result contain no hydrous minerals, are known as **granulites**.

In general, the coarser the overall grain size of a metamorphic rock, the more extreme the conditions, i.e. the higher the temperature and/or pressure, the higher the metamorphic grade, and the longer the time period under which metamorphism took place.

■ Is this explanation of the grain size variation of metamorphic rocks applicable to igneous rocks?

☐ No. In igneous rocks the grain size is generally related to the rate of cooling of the magma.

The terms used to describe regional metamorphic rocks are summarised in Table 8.1; their textures can be examined more fully in Activity 8.2.

Table 8.1   Major textural groups of regional metamorphic rocks.

Textural type	Nature of foliation	Grain size	
slate	very closely spaced, almost perfectly flat foliation surfaces	very fine	<<0.25 mm
phyllite	characteristics between slate and schist with a sheen of minute mica and/or chlorite flakes on wavy or wrinkled foliation surfaces	fine	0.25 mm
schist	moderately spaced undulating foliation surfaces, characteristically with abundant mica flakes	medium to coarse	0.25 to >2 mm
gneiss	more widely spaced undulating foliation surfaces with bands of felsic and mafic minerals	medium to coarse	0.25 to >2 mm
granulite	coarse-grained granular texture; no hydrous, platy minerals and lacking foliation	coarse	>2 mm
migmatite	layers and patches of felsic and mafic minerals (see Figure 8.5)	coarse	>2 mm

Activity 8.2   Textures in regionally metamorphosed rocks

This activity focuses on the textural character of a series of metamorphic rocks.

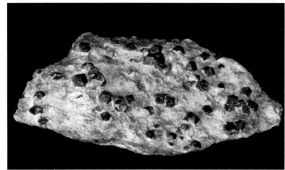

Figure 8.6   A classic regional metamorphic rock: well-formed garnet crystals (~1 cm) in a garnet mica schist.

The metamorphic rock shown in Figure 8.6 contains large (~1 cm), brownish-red crystals that have been exposed from the muscovite matrix. These are garnets, most of which are much larger than the average grain size of the rock. They are also well formed, with several flat faces developed on each crystal. Large crystals, such as these, in metamorphic rocks are called **porphyroblasts**, and the rock texture, **porphyroblastic**. (These are not to be confused with the phenocrysts of igneous rocks: porphyroblasts are formed in the solid state during metamorphism.)

Question 8.3

Recapping, how are phenocrysts formed? What is the textural term for a rock containing phenocrysts?

8.3 Metamorphic minerals and rock composition

Metamorphism normally involves little or no change in the overall chemical composition of a rock, apart from the expulsion of aqueous fluids and gases. However, the individual minerals within a metamorphic rock are *not* usually the same as those that were present in the parent rock before metamorphism. For instance, the chemical elements that make up the clay minerals in a mudstone become redistributed in new minerals, such as mica or chlorite, on metamorphism. With further increases in temperature and pressure, other minerals may develop, such as the garnets in garnet mica schist (Figure 8.6). A wide range of minerals may form during progressive stages of metamorphism, depending on the chemistry of the original rock and the temperature and pressure of metamorphism.

There are some rocks, however, in which no new minerals are formed by metamorphism. These are rocks made entirely of a single mineral, such as quartz or calcite, that continues to be stable under the new conditions. Rocks of this kind are termed **monomineralic**. In these two examples, the only elements involved are Si and O in quartz and Ca, C and O in calcite. During metamorphism, new crystals of either quartz or calcite grow together in the solid state by transfer of material from the original sedimentary grains.

■ Which sedimentary rocks consist entirely of (a) quartz and (b) calcite?

☐ Figure 7.15 shows that rock (a) would typically be a quartz sandstone and rock (b) would be a limestone.

Upon metamorphism, a quartz sandstone will become a **quartzite** (Figure 8.7a), and a limestone will become a **marble** (Figure 8.7b). Neither quartz nor calcite normally forms platy or elongate crystals when growing within a rock, so pure quartzites and marbles tend *not* to develop a strong foliation or lineation, and the individual grains are largely in random orientation with an equigranular texture. In practice, it may be difficult to identify such rocks in hand specimen as metamorphic unless their field context is known (or they are studied in thin section). Also, without foliation, such rocks could be the product of contact metamorphism or regional metamorphism, so it is important to take field relationships into account.

(a)

(b)

Figure 8.7 Monomineralic metamorphic rocks: (a) quartzite (RS 5) (5 cm); (b) marble (RS 17) (5 cm).

Activity 8.3   Metamorphism in monomineralic rocks

This activity investigates the mineralogy and fabric of a quartzite and a marble.

One of the primary controls on the minerals that form during metamorphism is the chemical composition of the parent rock; other controls are the temperature and pressure. Some metamorphic minerals can be good indicators of particular temperatures and pressures.

If you consider the progressive metamorphism of one particular kind of parent rock, such as a mudstone, then the minerals that crystallise during metamorphism will depend only on the temperature and pressure. Under low-grade conditions, the new minerals that form from the clay minerals and fine-grained quartz present in mudstone are mainly chlorite and muscovite. With increasing metamorphic temperature and pressure, some of these early formed minerals themselves begin to be transformed into new minerals, for example chlorite will change into biotite. At progressively higher grades, these minerals in turn will give way to other minerals, such as garnet, staurolite or kyanite.

As new minerals form, their character, especially in the case of micas, affects the development of foliation and metamorphic banding, as indicated in the textural classification outlined in Table 8.1. Perhaps the most obvious feature is the increase in grain size with increasing metamorphism. If metamorphism ceases at some point – when subsidence and burial stop – and there has been sufficient time for minerals to develop and chemical exchange to stabilise, it is said that the minerals are in **equilibrium**. The minerals present make up the **metamorphic assemblage**, which both reflects the temperature and pressure conditions at which metamorphic development ended, and depends on the overall rock composition.

■ Look at Figure 8.6. Which minerals do you think are present?

☐ The grey platy mineral that defines the foliation is mainly muscovite mica; the large brownish-red porphyroblasts are garnet. There are also some fine-grained quartz crystals (not easily visible).

The mineral assemblage of this rock comprises garnet, muscovite mica and quartz. It was probably derived by metamorphism of a mudstone originally composed of fine-grained clays and quartz. From its texture it is a schist, and as the most distinctive metamorphic minerals are garnet and mica, it can be called a garnet mica schist.

Question 8.4

Suppose that interbedded amongst some mudstones there was a basalt lava flow. Explain whether or not you would expect the mineral assemblage produced by metamorphism of the basalt to be the same as that produced by metamorphism of the mudstones.

The mineralogical and rock type changes during progressive regional metamorphism in rocks that were originally mudstones, sandstones and limestones are summarised in Figure 8.8. Clearly, the sequence of metamorphic minerals that form in mudstone compositions does not apply to sandstones or limestones. The diagram shows trends and very approximate temperatures at which the various changes occur. It is important to note that the temperatures shown on the vertical axis are for the *appearance* of the minerals shown (for metamorphism of mudstones); and once formed, some minerals persist to much higher temperatures. Also, since temperature, pressure and rock composition together control the formation of new minerals, Figure 8.8 cannot be used alone to decide the exact temperature at which a particular rock has formed. The nature of the original rock is also important: a metamorphosed mudstone will usually form a schist at medium grades, whereas a metamorphosed granite will usually form a gneiss.

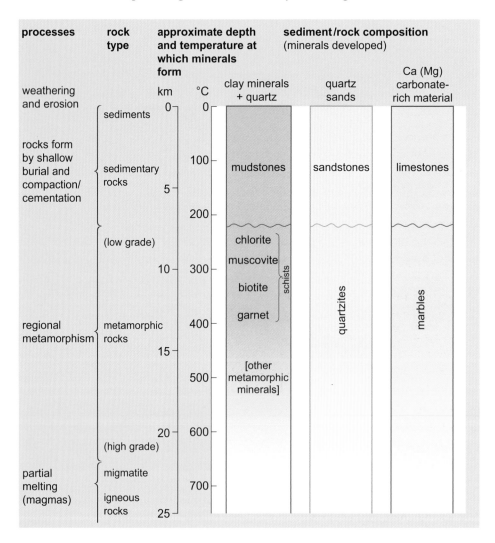

Figure 8.8 Mineralogical and rock type changes in progressive regional metamorphism of typical mudstones, sandstones and limestones. Depth scale appropriate for a geothermal gradient of 30 °C km^{-1}.

Some minerals formed at higher temperatures in both igneous and metamorphic rocks are highly susceptible to chemical attack at low temperatures, particularly under the influence of hydrothermal fluids or even weathering. Olivine, for example, is often transformed to serpentine (a hydrous magnesium silicate mineral) and iron oxide minerals. Once formed, however, most metamorphic minerals remain stable at lower temperatures and pressures, as rates of solid-state reactions slow down hugely with reduction in temperature. This allows metamorphic rocks to be found in pristine condition at the Earth's surface for millions, even billions, of years after they formed.

Activity 8.4   Influence of original rock composition on metamorphic rock produced

This activity reinforces your understanding of the relationship between metamorphic rocks and their origins.

8.4   Summary of Chapter 8

1   Metamorphic rocks are formed from pre-existing rocks by the growth of new minerals in the solid state (without melting) as a result of increased pressure and/or temperature.

2   Contact metamorphism occurs when hot magma is intruded into cooler country rocks to form a hard and splintery hornfels, which may be spotted (with diffuse patches of new minerals) and/or may contain porphyroblasts (larger crystals) that grew in random orientations.

3   Regional metamorphism occurs in rocks subjected to high pressures and temperatures during burial and tectonic activity in zones of crustal thickening associated with mountain building. New mineral growth responds to compression so that platy and elongate minerals line up more or less parallel to one another to produce a foliation or lineation.

4   In regionally metamorphosed rocks, the development of foliation and banding is used with grain size to describe the texture and classify the rock. At high pressures and temperatures, segregation of felsic and mafic minerals may give the rock a banded appearance.

5   Under extreme conditions of regional metamorphism, a rock may begin to melt to form a migmatite.

6   Metamorphism normally involves little or no change to the overall chemistry of a rock, apart from the expulsion of aqueous fluids and gases. However, except in the case of monomineralic rocks, the minerals of a metamorphic rock are not usually the same as those present in the parent rock before metamorphism.

7   The factors that control the minerals formed during metamorphism are the chemical composition of the parent rock, and the temperature and pressure to which the rock was subjected and remained at long enough for equilibrium between minerals to be attained.

8   The minerals occurring in a metamorphic rock, the metamorphic assemblage, reflect the particular conditions at the peak of metamorphism. Most metamorphic minerals subsequently remain stable at lower temperatures and pressures unless affected by fluids during hydrothermal activity or weathering.

8.5   Objectives for Chapter 8

Now you have completed this chapter, you should be able to:

8.1 Describe the differences between contact and regionally metamorphosed rocks.

8.2 Recognise the metamorphic textures developed with varying grades of regional metamorphism.

8.3 Identify the mineral assemblages of common metamorphic rocks.

8.4 Explain in general terms how the mineralogy of a metamorphic rock depends on the chemistry of the original rock from which it is derived.

Now try the following questions to test your understanding of Chapter 8.

Question 8.5

Considering the slate (Figure 8.4a) and the schist (Figure 8.4c), what makes you think that the schist probably formed under more extreme metamorphic conditions than the slate?

Question 8.6

Compare the garnet-bearing schist (Figure 8.4c) with the pyritic slate (MS I) of the Home Kit (also in the Digital Kit > Minerals > Pyrite > Crystals in slate). What are the similarities and differences between these two rocks? Try to explain the differences.

Question 8.7

Explain why at first sight you might misidentify a marble as an igneous rock. How would you recognise its true nature when you looked at its mineral content?

Chapter 9   Rocks in the field

Much of this book so far has focused on studying the minerals from which rocks are made and how these come together to form different rocks. You have examined a range of rock and mineral specimens in the Home Kit and the Digital Kit, and have developed some of the skills needed to identify them and interpret their origin. You now have many of the basic tools that you need to take your studies out into the field.

For most geologists, the field is the starting point for investigations – it is where rocks occur in context. A rock sample is not simply a granite, a dolerite or a sandstone; it may be part of an extensive pluton that extends for many kilometres; or a minor igneous intrusion that forms a sheet just metres across, bordered by different rock types; or it might be a sedimentary layer deposited in a lake, grading into a marine limestone above and a mudstone below. Immediately you can see that observing a rock in its context can be crucial for a fuller understanding of how it formed.

Observation in the field at the scale of an exposure (often metres to tens of metres in extent), possibly of a single rock face, involves not only identifying the rocks present, but also recognising the relationships between them. Various features may be present, such as bedding, faulting, and folding. Such field relationships can reveal the sequence of geological events, in particular the nature of the geological environment, any changes that took place, and the processes involved. Larger-scale investigations can lead to the geological history and structure of a region being deduced, and on a smaller scale, samples can be taken to the laboratory where sophisticated methods can provide evidence of the processes involved and their timing.

- ■ Imagine you arrive at a field locality, and start to observe the rocks. Which would you do first – look at the larger-scale features of the rocks or identify the rock layer that appears to be most prominent?

- ☐ It is always helpful to take a broader view first, looking for patterns and relationships between rock units, and then to identify the rock types.

Figure 9.1 shows examples of two field exposures. If you visited these localities in the field, what could you deduce about the rocks and the geology of the area?

Question 9.1

Looking at Figure 9.1a, what can you observe from the rocks in this exposure and predict about their likely relationships?

Question 9.2

Looking at Figure 9.1b, what could you say about the rocks making up the cliff face?

The investigation of a larger area (square kilometres in extent), comprising many separate exposures, requires mapping to connect the information deduced from individual exposures. Geological mapping places emphasis on the distribution and spatial relationships of rock units, the boundaries between them, the direction in which they trend, and their angle of dip. These aspects will be considered further in Chapters 10 to 12. Geological maps are helpful for getting to grips with geology on a much larger scale – up to that of whole countries and beyond.

(a)   (b)

Figure 9.1 (a) A vertical exposure of rock on the volcanic island of Tenerife. (b) A cliff face in Lyme Bay, Dorset. For use in Questions 9.1 and 9.2.

Activity 9.1 Rocks in the field

This activity involves watching the video *Rocks in the field* on DVD, which introduces you to some geology of Northern Ireland. It gives you an opportunity to appreciate the importance of studies within a field context where spatial and temporal relationships are important in deducing the geological story to be told from rocks.

9.1 Summary of Chapter 9

1 Field studies are the starting point for most geological investigations. Seeing rocks in a field context where spatial and temporal relationships may be determined helps in developing an understanding of the geological history and structure of an area. Samples collected from the field for laboratory inspection and analysis may reveal evidence of events and processes involved in their formation.

9.2 Objectives for Chapter 9

Now you have completed this chapter, you should be able to:

9.1 Appreciate that studying rocks in the field is the starting point from which an understanding of the geological structure and geological history of an area can be developed.

9.2 Recognise some of the more common features of rocks as they appear in the field.

Chapter 10   Landscapes and geology

10.1   Earth: a dynamic planet

The surface of the Earth's Moon (Figure 10.1) is pockmarked with millions of impact craters, as are the surfaces of many of the other planets and satellites of the Solar System. Yet when we look at the Earth, we see a very different landscape. Why is this? Why are so few impact craters visible on the Earth? We should expect that the Earth has collided with roughly as many asteroids or comets (per unit area) as the Moon, because they have occupied the same region of space for the past 4600 million years. One reason the Earth looks so different from other rocky planetary bodies in the Solar System is that its surface is constantly changing, due to the movement of its tectonic plates and its active volcanoes. Another reason is the fact that, unlike the other planets, the Earth possesses an atmosphere, water and living organisms in abundance. These agents physically disintegrate and chemically decompose the rocks and minerals of the Earth's surface by weathering; materials may also be eroded, to be transported and deposited elsewhere.

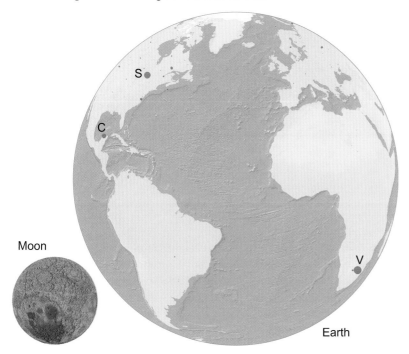

Moon

Earth

Figure 10.1   A view of Earth with known impact craters plotted (to scale), compared with a shaded relief map of the heavily cratered far side of the Moon (also to scale). V = Vredefort; S = Sudbury; C = Chicxulub.

Solid rock is seldom extensively exposed at the Earth's surface (Figure 10.2), but typically covered by soil and superficial deposits (Section 1.3.3). However, the form of a landscape can often tell the geologist a good deal about the underlying rocks, because landscapes are shaped by the processes of weathering and erosion on the one hand and deposition on the other. These processes are so inconspicuous on a day-to-day timescale that their importance is often underestimated, yet they are responsible for shaping the majority of the landscapes around us.

Rocks differ considerably in their resistance to erosion and weathering, so different rock types may be subject to **differential erosion**. In general, among the sedimentary rocks, limestones and sandstones are relatively resistant to erosion and tend to form higher ground with positive features such as cliffs and steep slopes, whereas less-resistant mudstones underlie the intervening valleys and seldom form exposures. Igneous and metamorphic rocks tend to be very resistant to erosion. The relationship between landform and geology is best studied in the field, though with increasingly sophisticated software, 3D visualisations allow some appreciation of this relationship, even on a computer screen. This chapter begins by looking at a landscape dominated by igneous rocks.

Figure 10.2 Arid landscape in Himachal Pradesh (NW India) with extensive rock exposure and little vegetation. Superficial deposits are mainly scree.

10.2 Landscapes and geology on the Isle of Skye

You saw on Figure 1.7 that intrusive igneous rocks (mainly granites) are abundant in Scotland. On the Bedrock UK Map (N), the heart of the Isle of Skye is dominated by two different types of intrusive rock: granites (shaded pink), and gabbros (shaded dark green). Both are labelled with the letter *G*, which marks them as Palaeogene in age.

Figure 10.3 is a simplified geological map of Skye. The rounded Red Hills form an area of relatively high ground to the north of the Strathaird Peninsula and are composed of hard, crystalline granite. The lower ground of the Strathaird Peninsula is underlain by much softer Jurassic sedimentary rocks capped in places by volcanic rocks. The sedimentary rocks weather more readily to form deeper soils and better farmland, while the volcanic lavas weather less readily and form the hills.

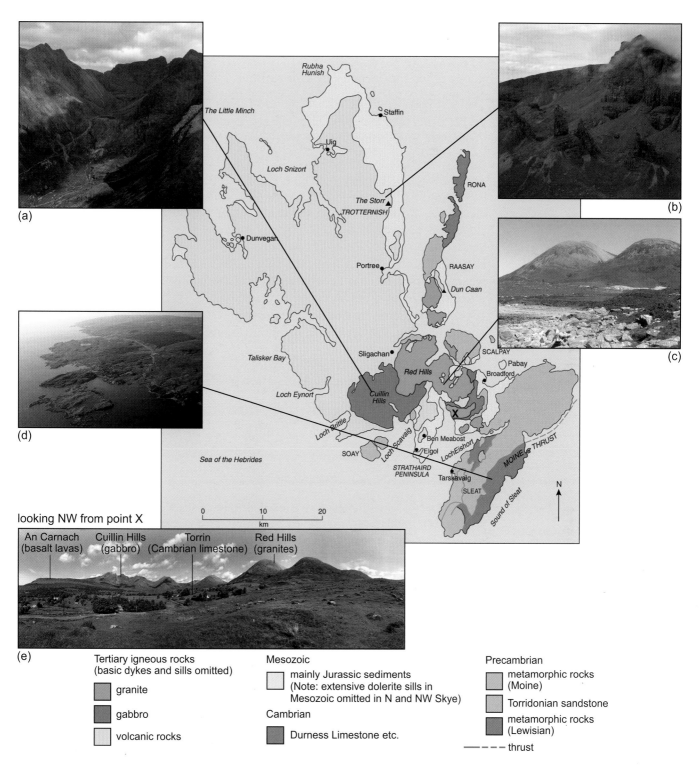

Figure 10.3 A simplified geological map of Skye, with images of landscapes characteristic of outcrops of different bedrock: (a) the Black Cuillin: carved from gabbro by glaciers; (b) the Storr: eroded cliffs on the edge of a plateau formed by Palaeogene basaltic lava flows; (c) the Red Hills: rounded granite mountains; (d) the Sleat Peninsula: Proterozoic sandstones and metamorphic rocks; (e) looking NW from point X on the map towards the Red Hills and Cuillin Hills. (a) and (b) reproduced with the permission of the British Geological Survey © NERC. All rights Reserved.

Activity 10.1   Relating topography to geology in southern Skye

The first part of this activity explains in detail how to construct a topographic profile using a topographic map extract. In the second part, you will add some geological detail to this profile by reference to a geological map extract.

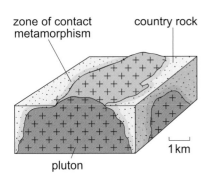

Figure 10.4   The three-dimensional shape of a pluton, showing the contacts with the country rocks, and the zone of contact/thermal metamorphism that surrounds it. A cross ornament is commonly used to denote granite, as is the colour red.

The margins of the granite intrusions that form the Red Hills are commonly marked by an abrupt change in the topographic gradient, termed a **break in slope**, where steep slopes underlain by resistant granite give way to the gentler landscape of the softer sedimentary rocks. The form of a typical pluton is shown in Figure 10.4. On each side of the pluton, the **contact** marking where the intrusion has been intruded into the country rocks slopes downwards away from its centre at a steep angle. The steep slopes at the edges of the Beinn na Caillich granite in the Red Hills suggest that this granite also has this typical form, and its roughly circular outcrop supports this idea.

Activity 10.2   Six contrasting landscapes on Skye

In this activity, you will learn how the geology of Skye influences the island's landscapes.

The Isle of Skye provides a striking example of how the underlying geology controls the landscape (Figure 10.3). The large mass of erosion-resistant granites forms the rounded Red Hills; the rugged Cuillin Ridge is carved from tough gabbro; flat-lying lavas form the plateaux of Trotternish and An Carnach, while the less-resistant sedimentary rocks to the south have been eroded more quickly and form lower ground. The picture for the rest of northern Scotland, North Wales and the English Lake District is broadly similar, with erosion-resistant igneous or metamorphic rocks forming the high mountains, and sedimentary rocks commonly forming the low ground. However, even subtler variations of rock type can strongly influence landscapes, as demonstrated in the next section.

10.3   Sedimentary strata in southern England

10.3.1   Landforms of gently dipping beds

The landscape of central southern England is gentler than that on Skye, reflecting the generally softer underlying sedimentary rocks and gently dipping strata. Figure 10.5 shows the topography of an area extending from Gloucestershire to Buckinghamshire, colour-coded to represent land of different elevations.

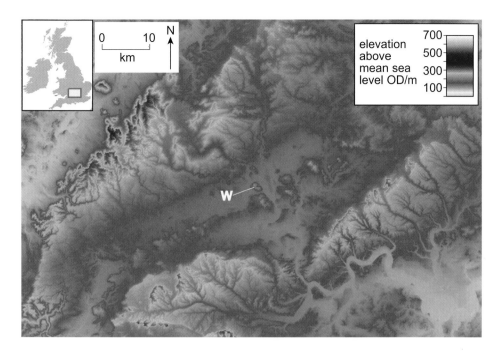

Figure 10.5 Digital Terrain Model (DTM) of central southern England, showing how elevation varies across the region. Key to colours shows elevation in metres above sea level; inset shows location of main figure relative to the rest of Britain; W marks Wytham Hill.

■ Where do areas of high and low ground occur?

☐ Two broad bands of high ground (yellow to red colours) run NE–SW across the map. Between these is a vale of low ground (green), split down the middle by a thin, discontinuous band of rather higher ground. The areas of low and high ground all trend NE–SW, and the uplands are dissected by river valleys.

Looking at the geological map for the same area (Figure 10.6), it is clear that the topography is mainly due to the underlying bedrock, which comprises successive strata trending NE–SW across the region. In the southeast, the resistant Cretaceous Chalk (K6 on the Bedrock UK Map (S)) forms the Chiltern Hills, while the Cotswold Hills in the northwest are capped by Mid Jurassic limestone (J3). More easily eroded Jurassic mudstones (e.g. Oxford Clay, J4, and Kimmeridge Clay, J6) underlie the low-lying vales. The stratigraphic unit between these (Corallian, J5) includes rubbly limestones, which are harder than the mudstones of J4 and J6, and hence form a low ridge separating them.

■ Is each of the two main ridges, the Chilterns and Cotswolds, topographically symmetrical in cross-section?

☐ No, they are both noticeably asymmetric. In each case, the sharp northwest boundary is marked by steep slopes (rapid colour changes on Figure 10.5). In contrast, the other flank slopes gently away towards the southeast, as shown by the gradual change in colours.

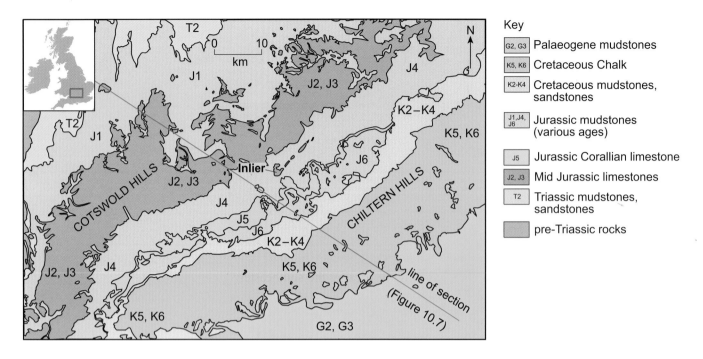

Figure 10.6 Simplified geological map showing bedrock geology of part of central southern England.

What causes this marked asymmetry? It results from the fact that the strata are not horizontal, but are tilted gently down towards the southeast (as shown in Figure 10.7). Geologists say that the strata **dip** southeast. William Smith's geological map of 1815 (Figure 1.9) gives an impression of the dip of the strata by the shading he used from the base to the top of the beds. Moving from northwest to southeast across the map in Figure 10.6, you encounter progressively younger strata in the same direction that they dip, a useful rule of thumb illustrated in Figure 10.8. Provided that the land surface is fairly flat, and the rocks have not been overturned (which can happen), this is a general rule:

Younger strata crop out in the direction of dip.

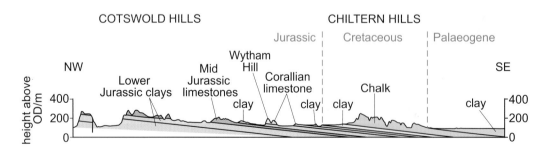

Figure 10.7 Simplified cross-section along the line of section marked on Figure 10.6. The vertical scale has been exaggerated 20 times relative to the horizontal scale to accentuate the topography and strata. Owing to this exaggeration, strata appear to be inclined more steeply (in reality, these strata dip southeastwards at less than 0.5°).

In fact, the progressively younger strata on the line from Edinburgh to London (Section 1.3.1) also reflect this general dip of the strata from northwest to southeast (or west to east) along much of this journey.

To define the attitude of a dipping bed, geologists specify the **angle of dip** (measured downwards from the horizontal), the **direction of dip**, and the **strike** of the bed (Figure 10.8). The strike of a dipping bed is the unique orientation of horizontal parallel lines that can be drawn on the surface of the bed (like the edge of a pool of water ponded against the surface). The strike, recorded as a compass direction (or 'bearing'), is by definition at right angles to the dip direction. Walking 'along the strike' of a bed means that you follow the trend of its outcrop in the landscape; in fact, the trends of both the Cotswold and Chiltern Hills follow the strike of the Mid Jurassic limestones (J2 and J3) and the Chalk (K5 and K6), respectively. The steep escarpments at their northwestern edges that cut through the strata are termed **scarp slopes** (Figure 10.9). The much gentler slopes that roughly parallel the southeastern dip of the strata are called the **dip slopes**. Dip and scarp slopes are very common in areas where gently dipping strata have differing resistance to erosion, and provide important information on the disposition of the rocks.

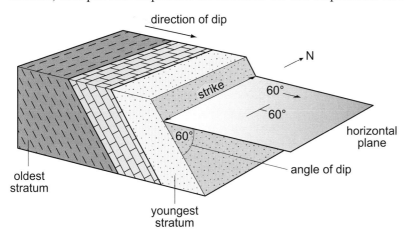

Figure 10.8   Block diagram of tilted strata illustrating the principles of strike and dip. The strike of a rock layer is the direction of the line formed by the intersection of a horizontal plane and a bedding plane. The dip of the layer is measured from the horizontal, in a vertical plane perpendicular to the strike. The symbols show two conventions used to indicate dipping beds on geological maps (an arrow pointing in the direction of dip, or a strike line with a tick on the down-dip side). Note the general rule that progressively younger strata are encountered in the direction of dip.

The feature marked with a W on the elevation map (Figure 10.5) is a distinct hill (Wytham Hill) that stands out northwest of the main line of the scarp formed by the outcrop of Corallian limestone (unit J5 on the Bedrock UK Map and Figure 10.6).

Question 10.1

(a) Comparing Figure 10.5 with Figure 10.6, which lithostratigraphic unit forms this hill?

(b) Explain why this hill rises above the surrounding vale.

The distinctive pattern of Wytham Hill on the geological map (Figure 10.6 and the Bedrock UK Map) shows an isolated outcrop of younger, Corallian limestone (J5) surrounded by older Kellaways and Oxford Clay Formations (J4). This feature is known as an **outlier**. The opposite situation, where an area of older rocks is surrounded by younger rocks, is termed an **inlier** (there is one large inlier of Mid Jurassic limestone about 6 km NE of Wytham Hill labelled on Figure 10.6). Both features may be produced by differential erosion (as at Wytham Hill), though commonly other factors are involved, such as faulting or an unconformity, as you will see later.

Part of the steep, west-facing scarp slope of the Cotswold Hills shown in Figure 10.9 can be located on the OS topographic map extract in Figure 10.10 by strips of closely spaced contour lines that depict steep slopes (e.g. at Nibley Knoll, 743956). Figure 10.11 shows how the relatively resistant limestones of the Inferior Oolite and Great Oolite Groups cap the hills here, forming the gentler dip slope. Note also that most of the strata in this sketch cross-section (apart from the Bridport Sand Formation) have been drawn with parallel tops and bases, thereby making them of constant thickness. This is typical of many stratigraphic units, at least over distances that are small compared with the total geographical extent of the unit. This is of great practical importance when constructing geological cross-sections, so the tops and bases of strata in vertical cross-sections are normally drawn parallel with each other. Only if you find information on the map to tell you that the units are not of constant thickness would you draw them otherwise. Finally, note the slight decrease in dip from west to east (exaggerated in this cross-section) of the Inferior Oolite Group.

Figure 10.9　View of the Cotswold escarpment, showing the steep scarp slope and gentler dip slope.

The Cotswold escarpment in the same area as Figure 10.10 produces a distinctive pattern on the corresponding 1 : 50 000 geological map (Figure 10.12). Here, the steep scarp slope cuts rapidly down through progressively older formations, which show up as relatively narrow bands on the map (e.g. at 741954, SW of Nibley Knoll). In contrast, broad outcrops of the same strata occupy the flat tops of the hills (e.g. around Symonds Hall Farm (790960)).

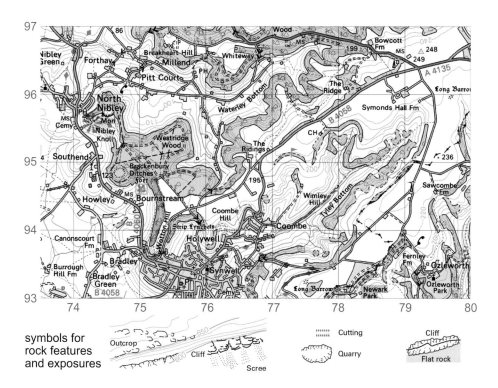

symbols for rock features and exposures

Outcrop

Cliff

Scree

Cutting

Quarry

Cliff

Flat rock

Figure 10.10 Extract from OS topographic map, grid square ST (31) 3719. Grid squares are 1 km across.

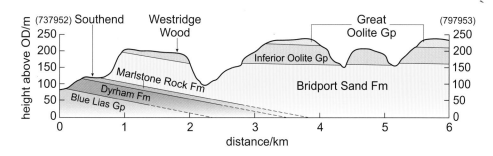

Figure 10.11 Sketch geological cross-section, comprising a topographic profile from 737952 to 797953, with subsurface geology sketched in below by extrapolating from the surface outcrop of the units.

This illustrates an important relationship between topographic slope and outcrop width in areas of gently dipping or horizontal strata:

> For horizontal or gently dipping strata of constant thickness, narrow, strip-like outcrops occur on steep slopes and wide outcrops occur on gentle slopes (Figure 10.13).

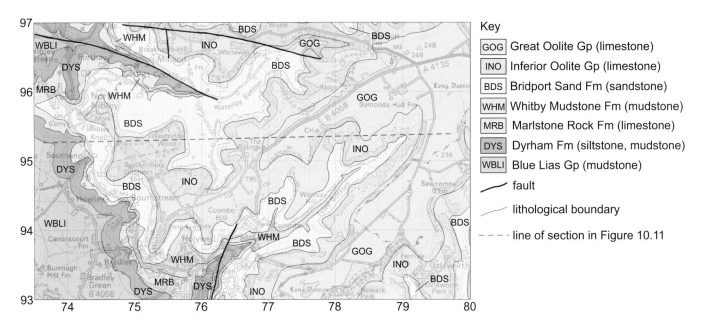

Figure 10.12   Extract from the 1 : 50 000 map of the bedrock geology of the Malmesbury area, showing the same area as Figure 10.10. The line of the geological cross-section in Figure 10.11 is marked by a dashed red line.

■   Looking at Figure 10.10, to what extent do you think that the geological outcrops in Figure 10.12 were mapped mainly by observing large rock exposures?

☐   There is very little indication of rock exposed at the surface (exposures such as cliffs, crags or scree) on Figure 10.10, so the outcrops of the units were likely deduced from other evidence (e.g. spring lines and boreholes). The only large exposure is on Nibley Knoll (745957), with a smaller one at 755967. However, there are smaller exposures of rock too small to be shown on the 1 : 50 000 OS map.

Another feature of the escarpment geology is that the outcrops of the strata around Nibley Knoll are not straight: in fact, the geological units trace out quite complex, irregular paths, in contrast to the straight lines depicted on Figure 10.13.

■   Compare the contours on Figure 10.10 with the outcrops of the strata on the geological map (Figure 10.12) around Nibley Knoll. Do they trace out the same path, or do the geological boundaries cut across the contours?

☐   The geological units follow the bulges and indentations of the contours very closely. In other words, the stratigraphic boundaries between the units are all *more or less parallel* to the contours.

Each contour can be imagined as the intersection between the topography and an imaginary horizontal plane at a specific height above mean sea level (Section 1.3.2). The fact that geological boundaries on this map follow the topographic contours indicates that the stratigraphic units must also be horizontal. This is an important relationship:

Where geological boundaries between strata are parallel to the topographic contours, the strata *must* be horizontal.

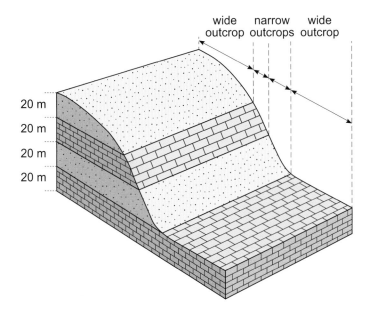

Figure 10.13 Block diagram illustrating how the width of outcrop of beds of a similar thickness can vary according to topographic slope.

Figure 10.14 illustrates this point. In Figure 10.14a, the layer-cake stratigraphy displayed at the front of the block model is comparable to the Cotswold escarpment edge. Cutting into this layer-cake model (Figure 10.14b) would be analogous to a river eroding a steep valley in the succession of horizontal strata, with the boundaries between the layers forming horizontal lines on the cut surfaces to make a V-shaped pattern that points up the valley, as illustrated in the plan view (Figure 10.14c).

Outcrop V-patterns thus provide another very important clue to geological structure because they tell us a great deal about the dip of strata. You have already seen that contours go around hills and ridges, and form Vs that point upstream (Figure 10.14), and you now also know that the outcrops of horizontal strata must *always* be parallel to contours (Figure 10.14c). Accordingly, a general rule follows:

Outcrops of horizontal or gently inclined strata usually form prominent V-shaped patterns that point upstream in valleys.

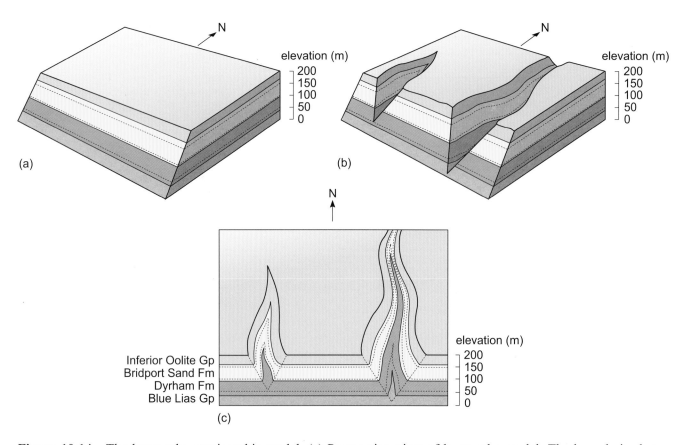

Figure 10.14 The layer-cake stratigraphic model. (a) Perspective view of layer-cake model. The boundaries between layers are parallel and horizontal, and so where they intersect the front (escarpment) edge, they are parallel to the contour lines, which are shown as dashed lines. (b) Two valleys are cut in the model. (c) A plan view – equivalent to a map view – of the model with valleys as in (b). Outcrops of the layers form a V-shaped pattern up each valley, parallel with the contours. Model colours are based on a simplified stratigraphy of the Cotswold scarp (Figure 10.12).

10.3.2 Regions with folded strata

About 50 km southwest of Nibley Knoll lies the distinctive broad ridge of the Mendip Hills, formed mainly of Carboniferous limestones that are around 180 million years older than the Jurassic limestones of the Cotswolds. Figure 10.15 shows part of the 1 : 50 000 geological map of the Bristol district (at reduced scale). The western Mendips are sharply defined by the outcrop of Carboniferous strata, which describe a tight arc like a hairpin bend.

- State the sequence of strata on the map along the line marked A–B on Figure 10.15.

☐ From the north, the sequence is: Hotwells Limestone Formation, 'chinastones', Clifton Down Limestone Formation, Burrington Oolite Subgroup, Black Rock Limestone Subgroup, Lower Limestone Shale, Portishead Formation, Lower Limestone Shale, Black Rock Limestone Subgroup, Burrington Oolite Subgroup, Cheddar Limestone Member, Cheddar Oolite Member, Clifton Down Limestone Formation, 'chinastones', Hotwells Limestone Formation.

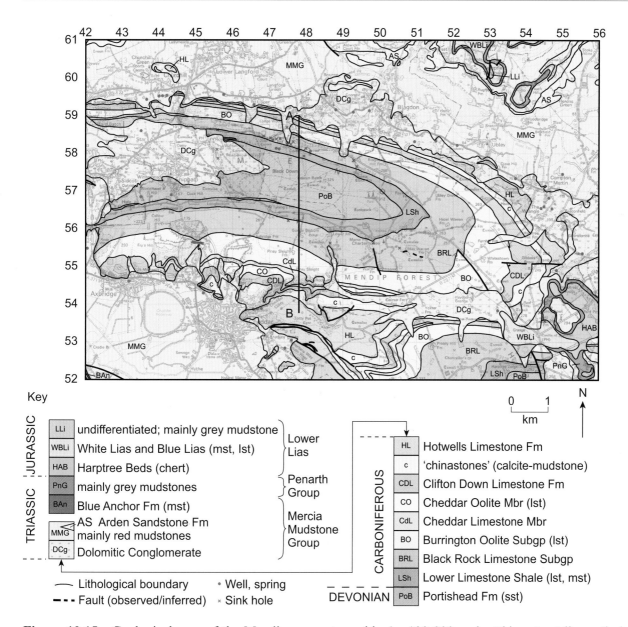

Figure 10.15 Geological map of the Mendips area at roughly 1 : 100 000 scale. This extract lies entirely within grid square ST (31), so these codes will be omitted from grid references to this map. Key includes units in lithostratigraphic order. Abbreviations: Fm: Formation; Mbr: Member; Subgp: Subgroup; lst: limestone; mst: mudstone; sst: sandstone.

■ How does the age of these strata change along this N–S line?

☐ From A in the north, the strata get progressively older; the oldest unit is the Devonian Portishead Formation in the core of the arc. However, continuing south along the line, this pattern reverses, with progressively younger strata cropping out towards B.

■ If the land surface here was fairly flat, what would this progression in strata ages suggest about the dip of beds along this line A–B?

□   Recalling that strata become younger in the direction of dip, this pattern suggests that the beds crossed by the northern part of the line are dipping north, while those south of Black Down (477574) dip to the south.

In fact, the Carboniferous and Devonian strata here have been **folded**: crumpled by tectonic forces that compressed the sedimentary layers. A series of folds is depicted in Figure 10.16, together with some of the terms used to describe them. A fold may be divided more or less evenly along its length into two **limbs**, one on either side of a line called the **fold axis**. The map pattern for the western Mendips is characteristic of an **anticline**, which is an arch-shaped fold with older rocks exposed in the core by erosion and progressively younger rocks exposed outwards on each limb. The reverse pattern is displayed in a **syncline**.

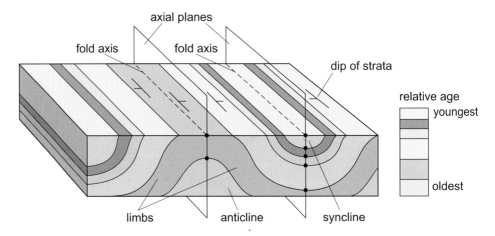

Figure 10.16   Anticlines and synclines in eroded strata. In an anticline, the limbs dip *away* from the fold axis. On a map, progressively older strata are found towards the axis of the fold. These relationships are reversed in synclines; the limbs dip *towards* the fold axis and on a map progressively younger strata are found towards the core of the fold. The fold axial plane cuts through the fold axes of successive layers.

Examples of folds at different scales are shown in Figure 10.17. Another clue from the map for the presence of a fold is the 'hairpin' pattern traced by the strata, which marks the fold **closure** (or 'nose'), where the two limbs meet. This pattern is not seen on Figure 10.16 because the fold axis is perfectly horizontal. However, horizontal folds in nature are uncommon, so in most cases such tight arcs are a useful indication of folded layers.

■   On Figure 10.15, compare the widths of the strata on the northern and southern limbs of the main anticline. Are they the same?

□   No. The strata have narrower outcrops on the north limb than on the south limb. In the east, where the strata close round the nose of the fold, the outcrops are even wider than on the southern limb.

In the absence of information on the exact dips of the strata, this change in width could have two alternative explanations (assuming a fairly flat land surface again):

- the sedimentary strata are actually thicker in the south than in the north, and become even thicker in the region of the fold closure

- the strata are the same thickness right around the fold, but dip at different angles, so that their widths on the map vary.

In this case, the latter is true; most sedimentary strata do not change thickness appreciably over short distances (Section 10.3.1). In fact, the anticline of the western Mendips is asymmetric, with steeper dips (55–70°) on the northern limb than on the southern limb (~30°), and this produces the asymmetric outcrop pattern on the map. Where the fold closes in the east, the strata dip even more gently (~20°) to the east. The cross-section in Figure 10.18 shows the form of the fold. The map pattern here illustrates another general rule:

Provided there are *no major changes in the thickness* of a rock formation, then as the dip *decreases*, the outcrop width of that formation on a map *increases*.

The V-patterns across river valleys you encountered in the previous section are useful clues to both the amount and direction of dip of strata from a geological map. Figures 10.19a and b illustrate an important rule for dip direction in valleys:

Outcrop V-shaped patterns of *dipping strata* on geological maps typically point in the direction of dip.

(a)

(b)

Figure 10.17 (a) Large-scale folds: an oblique aerial view of Sheep Mountain, an anticlinal ridge (brown, above and left of centre) approximately 17 km long, in Wyoming, USA. False-colour satellite image, draped over a digital terrain model. (b) Asymmetric folds on a smaller scale, Kangaroo Island, South Australia. Lens cap (top left) is 62 mm across.

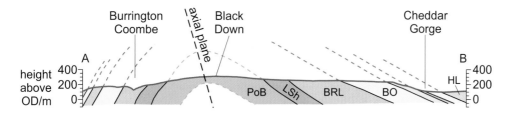

Figure 10.18 N–S cross-section (drawn to scale) through the western Mendips, showing the asymmetric form of the anticline and its inclined (dipping) axial plane. Horizontal scale of this section is twice that of Figure 10.15.

In addition, for a valley of a particular shape, the outcrop V-pattern becomes *less* pronounced as the dip of the strata *steepens* (Figure 10.19b and c).

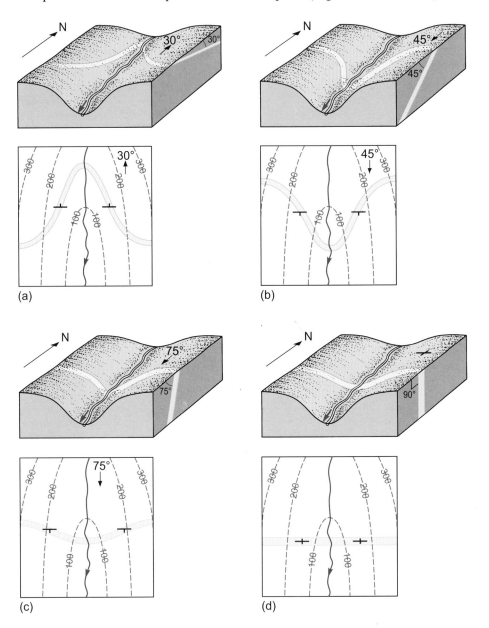

Figure 10.19 Block diagrams and associated map views illustrating V-shaped outcrop patterns of inclined beds. Dip symbols as in Figure 10.8, except in (d). (a) Beds dip upstream (north) at about 30°, producing a V-pattern pointing upstream. Note also that dipping beds cross the topographic contour lines. (b) Beds dip downstream (south) at about 45°, crossing contour lines to produce a V-pattern pointing downstream. (c) The beds here dip southwards more steeply (about 75°) than in (b), so although their V-pattern points the same way (south), the V-shape is much less pronounced. (d) Vertically dipping strata show no V-pattern in the outcrop as it crosses the valley. Note the dip symbol with a tick on both sides of the strike line, indicating the vertical dip.

■ On Figure 10.15, look carefully along the boundary between the Black Rock Limestone Subgroup and the Burrington Oolite Subgroup between easting grid lines 44 and 46 on the southern limb of the anticline. What does the outcrop pattern tell you about the strata here as they cross a N–S valley?

☐ There is a clear V-pattern in the boundary with its apex at 451556. The V-shape points south, so the strata must dip southwards; you can see from Figure 10.18 that on the line of section (about 3 km to the east) the strata dip about 25° towards the south.

There are almost no discernible V-patterns in strata on the northern limb of the anticline. This reflects mainly their much steeper dips (though it is also true that there are fewer deep valleys on the north flank of the Mendips where V-patterns would be seen).

Question 10.2

On the Bedrock UK Map (S), study the outcrop pattern of rock formations K4, K6, G3 and G4 between Corfe Castle (SY (30) 9682) and Shaftesbury (ST (31) 8623).

(a) In which direction are the strata dipping at Shaftesbury?
(b) Is the dip of the strata steeper near Corfe Castle, or around Shaftesbury?
(c) What is the major structure that results in the same stratigraphic units cropping out near Shaftesbury and Corfe Castle?

The structure referred to in Question 10.2 is the western end of the Hampshire Basin, whose edges can be roughly traced out on the map by following the outline of the Chalk (K6) from Brighton (TQ (51) 3204) northwestwards to Salisbury (SU (41) 1430), then round to Dorchester (SY (30) 6991), and back eastwards through the Isle of Wight. You will return to patterns of folded strata when you look at the overall structure of Britain in Chapter 11.

10.3.3   Unconformities in the landscape

Figure 10.20a shows a historic field sketch by Sir Henry De La Beche (1796–1855) of a quarry in the eastern Mendips; compare this with a modern photograph from the same site (Figure 10.20b). The sketch clearly shows horizontally bedded strata overlying dipping beds of rock along a sub-horizontal surface. The flat-lying, beige rocks above are oolitic limestones laid down in shallow seas roughly 175 million years ago (during the Jurassic Period), whereas the dipping grey rocks below (also limestones) are much older, and were deposited during the Carboniferous Period about 340 million years ago. This is obviously not a typical 'layer-cake' stratigraphy: it appears that strata representing some 165 million years are missing! The fossils in the upper and lower beds are very different, supporting the impression of a large time gap between the two sets of strata. It is worth reconstructing the sequence of events required to produce this geological exposure. Firstly, around 340 million years ago, the grey limestones were deposited in horizontal layers, gradually hardening into rock as they were buried under other sediments. Some time after this, these beds were tilted by earth movements so that they dipped at a moderately steep angle. A large amount of

a. Inferior Oolite.
b. Arenaceous parting.
c. Carboniferous Limestone.

(a)

(b)

Figure 10.20   (a) Field sketch of the Vallis Vale unconformity by Sir Henry De La Beche. ('Arenaceous' means 'sandy'.) (b) Photograph of the same angular unconformity, exposed in a different orientation at the Vallis Vale site.

time (including the whole of the Permian and Triassic Periods) elapsed, during which these uplifted, tilted rocks were eroded down to the sub-horizontal surface that cuts across the top of the dipping beds. About 175 million years ago, the beige, oolitic limestones were then deposited as horizontal beds on top of the tilted, eroded grey limestones as a shallow sea submerged the land surface, since when they have been lithified and uplifted to their present position.

You saw in Section 1.1 that the Principle of Superposition determines the order in which sedimentary rocks are deposited, but it does not imply that all layers have been deposited continuously over time. Indeed, if the geological record of a particular area were thought of as a pile of manuscript pages for a book, you would find that several chapters were absent – as if they had never been written or had been removed. A major gap in the rock record is referred to as an **unconformity**; it can be identified in the field by an erosional surface, like the subhorizontal surface in the quarry, between rocks of markedly different ages. An unconformity indicates that there was a break in the deposition of sediments and a period of erosion between the rocks above and below.

When the beds above and below an erosion surface have different dips (Figure 10.20), this is known as an **angular unconformity**. However, although an unconformity is evidence of a major gap in the geological record, there is no way of knowing how long a period of time that gap represents – unless accurate ages for the rocks above and below the unconformity can be obtained.

How might you identify a less well-exposed unconformity than that in Figure 10.20? Unconformity surfaces commonly separate rocks of different age and physical character, so the unconformity may be marked by a break in slope between a more resistant rock (forming higher ground) and a weaker rock that has been more heavily eroded. The two rock types might also have different permeabilities, so that water sinks easily through one rock (e.g. limestone) but cannot pass through the other (e.g. mudstone). Hence some unconformities may be marked by a line of springs (**spring line**), where water seeping through permeable rock meets impermeable rock beneath the unconformity. Other unconformities may result in a line of **sinkholes**, where streams running over impermeable rock cross the unconformity and sink quickly down into the permeable strata beneath. Numerous springs and sinkholes occur in the Mendips area, especially along the northern flank of the Mendips. Study the geology associated with the springs marked around Compton Martin (grid square 5457) and westwards towards point A (478590) in Figure 10.15.

■   Describe the form of the outcrop of the Dolomitic Conglomerate unit, part of the Mercia Mudstone Group, between easting lines 44 and 55 along the northern limb of the western Mendips anticline in Figure 10.15.

☐ This unit has a very irregular form, as if paint has been spilt across the neat outcrop patterns below. It runs broadly along the boundary between the Carboniferous rocks outlining the anticline and the red mudstones of the Triassic Mercia Mudstone Group, but encroaches onto the units onto both sides of the boundary in broad lobes and narrower tongues.

The boundaries of this unit cut boldly across the parallel stratigraphic boundaries of several underlying Carboniferous formations. This represents a clear angular relationship. You could imagine removing the paint-like blob of Triassic conglomerate to find the Carboniferous strata continuous underneath, all along the northern limb of the anticline. Since there are no bold lines marking faults along the boundaries of the Triassic rocks, this map relationship must represent an angular unconformity. The Triassic conglomerate, in fact, represents lobe-shaped deposits of coarse sediment eroded off the adjacent uplifted hills of Palaeozoic rock – the Carboniferous and Devonian rocks of the Mendips anticline. These conglomerates were rapidly piled up against the hills, and filled in steep valleys on their flanks, forming the distinctive 'tongues' pointing in towards the anticlinal axis. A cross-section down one of these valley tongues of conglomerate is shown in Figure 10.21.

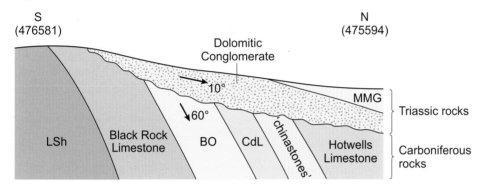

Figure 10.21   Sketch cross-section along the valley from 476581 to 475594 (see Figure 10.15). Note the major difference in the dips above and below the erosion surface, and the 'wavy line' commonly used to symbolise an unconformity.

Because the outcrop of the Triassic Dolomitic Conglomerate unit is so irregular, in places the red mudstones of the Mercia Mudstone Group directly overlie the Carboniferous rocks, for instance at 441593 and between 424558 and 448550 (on the southern limb of the anticline).

■ Do the red mudstones of the Mercia Mudstone Group also overlie the Carboniferous rocks on an unconformity, or is this contact a conformable one?

☐ In both locations, the base of the red mudstones unit cuts across the boundaries between strata in the underlying Carboniferous rocks, so this unit also overlies the older, folded rocks along an angular unconformity surface.

In fact, the base of the red mudstones unit roughly follows the topographic contours of the area, outlining the high ground occupied by the anticline. This in itself suggests that the dip of the strata in the Triassic rocks (and hence the unconformity surface) is almost horizontal.

10.3.4 Faults in the landscape

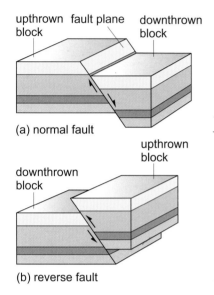

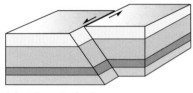

(a) normal fault

(b) reverse fault

(c) strike-slip fault

Figure 10.22 Some common types of fault, distinguished by the relative motion of the blocks either side of the fault plane. This motion may be dip-slip normal (a), or dip-slip reverse (b), or strike-slip (c).

When rocks deform, they may bend into folds where the strata are still continuous, or they may break and move relative to each other along lines of fracture (faults). The direction of relative motion allows faults to be divided into three main types (Figure 10.22). The surface along which movement has taken place is called the **fault plane**. If the fault movement has a vertical component along the dip of the fault plane (Figure 10.22a and b), the fault is referred to as **dip-slip**; the example shown in Figure 10.22a is a dip-slip **normal fault** and the example in Figure 10.22b is a dip-slip **reverse fault**. A **thrust** is a reverse fault with a low dip (<45°). If the displacement has been horizontal, however, parallel to the strike of the fault plane, the fault is referred to as a **strike-slip** fault (Figure 10.22c). You should realise, however, that faults can have both vertical and horizontal components to their movement so that few faults are pure dip-slip or pure strike-slip.

On geological maps, faults are typically represented by bolder lines than those for the lithological boundaries between different rock units. Major faults commonly juxtapose very different rocks, so they are conspicuous on maps as abrupt changes in colour and, in many cases, outcrop patterns. (You will look at some examples on the Bedrock UK Map in Chapter 11.) In the field, however, many faults are not easily visible, being cloaked by vegetation or superficial deposits. What clues can a geologist glean from the landscape to reveal their presence?

During earthquakes, slip on active faults may create a **fault scarp** where one block has slid down relative to another (Figure 10.23a), or offsets of linear features such as ridges, streams, roads and fences (Figure 10.23b). However, most landscape clues to faults result from the juxtaposition of two rock units with different properties, just as at an unconformity (Section 10.3.3). Hence, lines of springs or sinkholes are common clues to faults, marking the change in surface drainage from dry land underlain by a permeable rock (e.g. limestone) to boggy land with surface streams over impermeable strata. Faults separating rock types with a different resistance to weathering are usually marked by a break in slope. In some cases, the fault scarp is maintained by this differential erosion, and rivers cross the fault line at waterfalls. In faults that have been active over long periods, these rivers may cut steep gorges back into (i.e. upstream of) the fault scarp, as the erosional power of the river is strongly focused on the scarp at the waterfall. However, not all waterfalls and gorges are the result of faulting (Box 10.1).

(a)   (b)

Figure 10.23   Landscape clues to faults: (a) dip-slip fault scarp (about 4 m high) in Colca Canyon, Peru, caused by an earthquake in 1991; (b) a fence offset on a strike-slip fault during the San Francisco earthquake (18 April 1906).

Box 10.1   The smoke that thunders: Victoria Falls

Waterfalls and gorges arise in a variety of geological situations. Some gorges (e.g. Niagara, which marks the border between USA and Canada) are cut back from escarpments that simply mark the edge of an outcrop of particularly resistant rock. Other gorges result from efficient downcutting by a large river through a region undergoing rapid tectonic uplift; both the Indus and Brahmaputra rivers have incised deep gorges into the Himalayan mountain range at its western and eastern ends, respectively. The Grand Canyon is carved into a wide region (the Colorado Plateau) that experienced uplift around 17 Ma ago, in the Miocene Epoch.

In southern Africa, Victoria Falls (Mosi-oa-Tunya, or 'the Smoke that Thunders') is a waterfall 1.7 km wide that drops about 100 m into the Batoka Gorge, etched into the surrounding basalt plateau by the Zambezi River (Figure 10.24a). The Batoka Gorge runs for over 100 km downstream south and east through the basalt highlands, following a bizarre, zigzag course that coincides with the traces of numerous faults in the basalt (visible on Figure 10.24a). The current theory for the origin of the gorge and waterfall is that, a few million years ago, the lower portion of the Zambezi River cut back into the uplifted basalt plateau and 'captured' (i.e. linked up with) a river that ran across the top of the plateau. The point at which they joined was an abrupt step in the river's gradient, the original waterfall, which was probably a considerable distance southeast of the present Victoria Falls. As the Zambezi River swiftly cut back into the basalt, the site of the waterfall migrated upstream to its present position, exploiting the numerous faults as lines of weakness. The gorge immediately south of the falls owes its zigzag shape to the fact that all the major faults in this region trend E–W or NE–SW, so the river has had to cut first one way, then the other, along these lines of weakness (like a sailing boat tacking against the wind). The wide chasm marking the line of the falls is one of these faults.

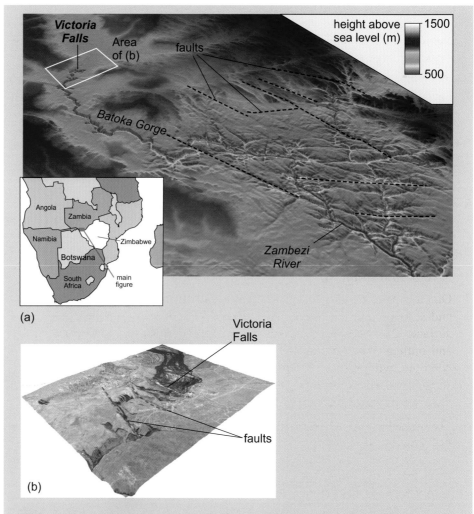

Figure 10.24 Features of the middle Zambezi River. (a) Batoka Gorge, downstream of Victoria Falls, appears as a conspicuous blue feature in the reddish colours that mark the high basalt plateau in this digital elevation model of northern Zimbabwe and southern Zambia. Numerous fault lines in the basalt are visible as furrows in the landscape; several have been exploited by the Zambezi, resulting in its present jagged course. (×2 vertical exaggeration.) (b) Oblique aerial view northwards to Victoria Falls over the zigzag gorges downstream. This image is a photograph taken from the International Space Station, draped over a digital elevation model, with no vertical exaggeration. The line of the falls trends approximately 105° ESE.

10.4   Summary of Chapter 10

1   The shape of much of the Earth's land surface is profoundly influenced by the underlying geology.

2   Earth's changing landscapes are the result of dynamic interactions between numerous processes that modify the land surface (e.g. weathering and erosion) and the bedrock geology.

3   The geologist can use information from landforms and isolated rock
    exposures in the field to interpret the underlying geology, as well as
    evidence from topographic maps or digital elevation models of the
    landscape.

4   Landscapes in the north and west of Britain, characterised by igneous and
    deformed metamorphic rocks, are typically rugged and mountainous. The
    Cuillin and Red Hills on Skye are impressive examples of mountains
    formed of resistant igneous rocks; areas of gentler topography on the
    island are underlain by sedimentary rocks. Stepped plateaux reflect their
    foundation of flat-lying basalt lavas.

5   The subtler landscapes of southern and eastern Britain reflect the gently
    dipping, softer sedimentary strata beneath. Steeper scarp slopes form where
    the land surface cuts down abruptly through successive strata.

6   Conformable strata become younger in the direction of dip (unless they
    have been overturned).

7   Outcrop patterns on geological maps result from the intersection of strata
    and structures in the underlying bedrock with the complex topographical
    surface. Differential erosion of gently dipping strata may produce inliers
    and outliers. The outcrops of horizontal strata run parallel to topographic
    contours, with V-shaped patterns pointing upstream in valleys. Outcrop V-
    shaped patterns of dipping strata in valleys tend to point in the direction of
    dip, and patterns become less pronounced as strata dips steepen.

8   Geological features such as igneous intrusions, major folds, unconformities
    and faults can be recognised and interpreted from the pattern of rock
    outcrops appearing on geological maps. Few fold axes are horizontal, so
    most folds are defined by a distinct curve of lithological boundaries on a
    map where the fold closes. Angular unconformities cut across older strata
    as irregular lines; many faults are marked by abrupt changes in colour
    where different geological units are juxtaposed.

9   Unconformities and faults may be inferred from clues in the landscape,
    such as breaks in slope, spring lines or scarps.

10.5   Objectives for Chapter 10

Now you have completed this chapter, you should be able to:

10.1 Draw simple topographic profiles across Ordnance Survey maps and
sketch simple geological cross-sections.

10.2 Use evidence from topographic and geological maps to recognise
features such as breaks of slope and spring lines, and infer the presence of
geological structures such as boundaries between different rock types, inliers,
and dip and scarp slopes.

10.3 Explain the relationship between the dip and strike of beds, and how the
angle of dip affects the width of outcrop on simple geological maps.

10.4 Deduce the regional dip and strike of an area from the outcrop pattern
and the relative ages of rocks.

10.5 Recognise major fold structures and correctly identify the type of fold as an anticline or syncline from outcrop patterns on geological maps.

10.6 Identify unconformities and faults from landscape features and outcrop patterns on geological maps.

Now try the following questions to test your understanding of Chapter 10.

Question 10.3

On the Bedrock UK Map (S), look at the Carboniferous rocks of the South Wales coalfield (units C2, C4, C5, C6 and C7), in particular from Llangynidr (SO (32) 1519) to Llanishen ST (31) 1782, about 5 km south of Caerphilly (ST (31) 1687).

(a)   Which way are the strata (beds C2, C4, C5, C6 and C7) dipping between Llanishen and Caerphilly?

(b)   Which way are the strata dipping between Llangynidr and just west of Abertillery (SO (32) 2005)?   SE

(c)   What major structure occurs between Llanishen and Llangynidr?

(d)   What is the general strike direction of the strata between Ammanford (SN (22) 6312) and Brynmawr (SO (32) 1912)?

(e)   What is the strike direction between Margam (SS (21) 8086) and Caerphilly?

Now look at the outcrop pattern between Risca (ST (31) 2491) and Blaenavon (SO (32) 2508).

(f)   What is the general strike direction in this area?

(g)   What is the dip direction in this area?

Question 10.4

Many of the rock types in the South Wales coalfield are quite resistant rocks: the Lower Old Red Sandstone Group (D1), the Millstone Grit Group (C4), and the Pennant Sandstone Formation (C7) are all mainly hard sandstones, while the Carboniferous Limestone Groups (C2) are dominated by tough limestone. The Coal Measures (C5, C6) also contain sandstones. Figure 10.25 is a cross-sectional sketch from Llanishen (south) to Brecon (north), showing topographic features and indicating some of the strata at outcrop. Complete this cross-section by drawing in the boundaries between C7 and C4–C6, between C4–C6 and C2, and between C2 and D1.

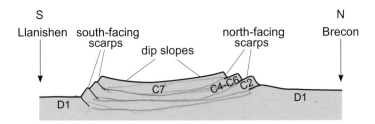

Figure 10.25 For use with Question 10.4. Brecon is at SO (32) 0428.

Question 10.5

Describe, and suggest two possible reasons for, the differing width of outcrop on the north and south limbs of the South Wales coalfield.

Chapter 11   The geology of Britain

11.1   Reading the Bedrock UK Map

In Section 1.4, you were introduced to the basic features of the Bedrock UK Map. Since then, you have encountered other geological maps at different scales and have started to use the Bedrock UK Map to interpret the geology of Britain. This section briefly introduces some more features of the map that will further enhance your understanding of geology.

11.1.1   Dividing sedimentary strata

In the index to the Bedrock UK Map, boxes representing successive sedimentary units are stacked on top of each other in order of age, following the Principle of Superposition. The lowermost units are the oldest and the uppermost are the youngest. Some Periods – such as the Devonian – are divided into three *time* divisions: Early, Mid and Late; the *rock* strata that correspond to these time divisions are referred to as Lower, Middle and Upper, respectively. Hence, Upper Devonian strata (rocks) were deposited during the Late Devonian (time).

■   A gap appears in the main lithostratigraphic column on the Bedrock UK Map (S) in Mid Devonian time, where Middle Devonian strata would lie. What does this gap represent?

☐   This gap marks a major unconformity (Section 10.3.3). In fact, all the distinct gaps between boxes mark major unconformities. Note that rocks *were* laid down during the Mid Devonian in some places, for instance in NE Scotland (unit D2 on the Bedrock UK Map (N)).

The colours of some units (e.g. bright yellowish-green for Chalk) are inherited from earlier editions of the map, but units within a particular Period typically show similar hues. However, several wedge-shaped units of contrasting colours occur in the lithostratigraphic index; an example is the Aymestry Limestone Fm within the Ludlow Shales (S3). These wedges represent thinner units of a different rock type to the main unit; the colour of the wedge generally reflects the rock type (e.g. blue for limestone and orange for sandstone). The wedge shape denotes that these units are less extensive than the main units, and typically discontinuous. Such units may pinch out and disappear abruptly, as the Aymestry Limestone (blue) does at SO (32) 4274 on the Bedrock UK Map (S).

The Aymestry Limestone unit is a **formation** (abbreviated to Fm), but there are smaller units of sedimentary strata. The smallest unit (too small to be shown on the Bedrock UK Map) is an individual *bed* of a particular rock type, separated from those above and below by bedding planes. Beds may be grouped together into units called **members** (Mbr); members may be grouped into formations; and formations may be grouped into **groups** (Gp) or subgroups. Formal unit names are denoted by upper-case first letters, for example the Llanberis Slates Fm (E1). These divisions of sedimentary strata are made on the basis of lithology; boundaries are commonly defined at surfaces where the rock type changes in some distinct way (e.g. composition, grain size, colour or structures). Generally, this reflects a change in the process of deposition and, commonly, a hiatus or break in sedimentation, which may be an unconformity. Historically, major breaks between strata have been used to divide up the lithostratigraphy into Periods and Epochs, which explains why rock units coincide with these intervals of time. Dating these breaks directly is difficult, so in any one area it is the rocks themselves that are used to define the boundaries of Periods, Epochs and Ages.

Note that the lithostratigraphic index is not to scale in terms of time or strata thickness. For instance, the boxes for units J2 to J7 are of identical height in the index to the Bedrock UK Map (S), but look on this map between Cheltenham (SO (32) 9523) and Swindon (SU (41) 1585) where these units all have a roughly constant, gentle dip to the southeast across relatively gentle topography.

- ■ What do the relative widths of the outcrops of units J2 to J6 in this area indicate?

- ☐ As all the units dip at the same constant angle southeastwards, the different outcrop widths must mean that the units have different thicknesses.

In fact, if the land surface is assumed to be flat, then the relative widths of the outcrops roughly correspond to the relative thicknesses of the units. Hence the Corallian Group (J5) is much thinner than the Great Oolite Group (J3).

11.1.2 Beneath the surface: cross-sections

Cross-sections at the bottom of the Bedrock UK Map sheets present current interpretations of the major subsurface structures. The lines along which the sections are constructed are marked as thin black lines on the main map, and labelled at each end (e.g. 'LINE OF SECTION 1' at TV (50) 6091). Notice that these lines are straight over long distances, but change direction in places (e.g. in central London at TQ (51) 3682. This is because cross-sections are most often drawn perpendicular to the strike of strata to show structures, such as folds, as clearly as possible, and depict the maximum dip of the strata. In fact, although the horizontal scale of these sections is the same as the main map (1 : 625 000), the vertical scale has been increased (×2), so the dips on the cross-sections are steeper than the true dips. This method of **vertical exaggeration** is common when presenting cross-sections, as it accentuates the structures. The true values of the exaggerated dips are depicted in a 'dipmeter', a small diagram to the left of Section 1 on the Bedrock UK Map (S).

The cross-sections are drawn mainly from surface information, such as the extent and dip of mapped rock units, extrapolated to depth using assumptions about strata thicknesses and successions. However, additional information on the vertical stratigraphy at certain points is available from boreholes drilled to various depths all over the UK, and also from geophysical methods that probe the subsurface to give a rough picture of the form and nature of rock units at greater depths. Such methods are invaluable in showing the form of igneous bodies such as the Dartmoor granite (near the right-hand end of Section 2 on the South sheet), the depths of older rocks known collectively as 'basement', and the presence of faults.

Question 11.1

For the geological features (a) to (e) described below and pictured in Figure 11.1, match each to a feature or location named on one of the cross-sections on the Bedrock UK Map. In each case, identify the feature.

(a) A vertical mafic dyke of Palaeogene age (Figure 11.1a) that is intruded into Triassic and Jurassic sediments (North sheet).

(b) A zone with Moine Supergroup rocks (X1, yellow) overlying slices of Lewisian Gneisses (A1), Durness Gp limestones (E3), Ardvreck Gp sedimentary rocks (E1–2), and finally Torridon Group strata (X or X1, pale brown) to the west (Figure 11.1b) (North sheet).

(c) Chalk sea cliffs (Figure 11.1c) (South sheet).

(d) A gently dipping fault overlain by metamorphic schists (Figure 11.1d) of probable Devonian age (South sheet).

(e) A distinct ridge of Neoproterozoic sandstone (Figure 11.1e) (part of X, pale beige), faulted against Ordovician and Silurian sedimentary strata (South sheet).

(a)   (b)   (c)

(d)   (e)

Figure 11.1   (a) A mafic dyke; (b) Durness limestones overlain by darker Lewisian gneisses; (c) Chalk sea cliffs; (d) schists of probable Devonian age; (e) Neoproterozoic sandstones forming a distinct ridge. (b), (c) and (e) reproduced with the permission of the British Geological Survey © NERC. All rights Reserved. (For use with Question 11.1.)

11.2   Exploring geological features on a map

Many geological maps display, at first glance, bewildering complexity, even in a simplified form (Figure 1.7). These complicated surface patterns result from processes in the rock cycle (Figure 5.3) that constantly recycle and modify the Earth's constituent materials. The rest of this chapter summarises how to recognise major geological features from outcrop patterns using the Bedrock UK Map and the Geological Map of Britain and Ireland (Figure 1.7). At the scales of these maps, you can treat the ground surface as essentially a horizontal plane because, at the scale of the Bedrock UK Map (1 : 625 000), Ben Nevis (1343 m high) would be only about

$$\frac{1343 \text{ m}}{625\,000} = 0.0021 \text{ m} = 0.21 \text{ cm high,}$$

and less than one-tenth of that at the scale of Figure 1.7 (about 1 : 7 000 000). Remember that the strike of the strata runs parallel to the stripes of outcrop on the map, and the direction of dip is at right angles to this strike direction.

11.2.1   Dipping strata

Figure 1.7 shows the outcrop of Jurassic rocks as a single large (bright blue) band across England. Figures 10.5 and 10.6 showed that the topography of central southern England reflects the very gently dipping Mesozoic bedrock strata. North of Nottingham, the strike of the Jurassic outcrop swings round to roughly north–south, with Cretaceous (bright-green) rocks to the east, while to the west are Triassic (dark pink), Permian (beige) and Carboniferous (pale blue) rocks.

■   Considering this, what is the general direction of dip for the Jurassic rocks of northern England?

☐   Since progressively younger strata (Carboniferous to Cretaceous) occur from west to east, all these strata in northern England must be dipping to the east. Thus the regional dip of the Jurassic rocks of northern England is also to the east, towards the North Sea Basin.

11.2.2   Folded strata

Again on Figure 1.7, look at the outcrop pattern of the Cretaceous and Palaeogene rocks in southeast England. You have already seen that there is a syncline in the Hampshire Basin (Section 10.3.2), where younger Palaeogene strata are almost completely surrounded by older Cretaceous strata.

■   What kind of structure lies beneath London?

☐   The Jurassic strata north and west of London are dipping to the southeast and are overlain by younger Cretaceous beds. London lies on even younger Palaeogene beds, but south of London the Cretaceous reappears. Therefore London must also lie in a synclinal fold. This is known as the London Basin.

■ Can you tell from Figure 1.7 what kind of structure lies between London and the south coast?

□ No. All the beds here are Cretaceous (bright green) in age.

Now look at the area south of London on the Bedrock UK Map (S). Here, the Cretaceous strata are subdivided into six separate units (K1–K6).

Question 11.2

Consider a journey from Lewisham (TQ (51) 3775) via East Grinstead (TQ (51) 3937) to Brighton (TQ (51) 3204) over the Weald area of Sussex and Kent. Look at the sequence of Cretaceous strata over which you would travel.

(a) What is the general strike direction of the beds between London and East Grinstead?

(b) Do you cross onto older or younger beds going from Lewisham to East Grinstead? In which direction do they dip?

(c) Do you cross onto older or younger beds going from East Grinstead to Brighton? Do they dip in the same direction as the beds to the north of East Grinstead?

(d) On Figure 11.2, which represents the land surface profile from London to Brighton, roughly sketch in the direction of dip of the beds. Since the scale here is 1 : 625 000, do not try to show the strata accurately. Can you see what structure underlies the Weald?

(e) Find the three small outcrops of the Purbeck Group (K1) in the Weald. Is their location consistent with the overall structure of the Weald?

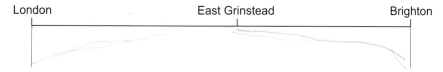

Figure 11.2 Section line from London to Brighton. (For use with Question 11.2.)

Southeast England is therefore underlain by three broad folds: the synclines of the Hampshire and London Basins separated by the Weald anticline. Moving northwestwards onto rocks older than the Jurassic, the pattern of folding becomes more complex.

11.2.3 Unconformities

You saw in Section 10.3.3 that unconformities can be recognised from map evidence at a scale of 1 : 50 000. However, some major unconformities can also be identified on even smaller-scale maps such as Figure 1.7. When unconformities represent a substantial time gap, as in the Mendip Hills (Section 10.3.3), they typically mark major events in the geological history of an area and may correlate with events at a plate tectonic scale. The unconformity surface on the flank of the Mendips anticline is quite irregular. This is because the younger sediments were deposited on an ancient landscape with considerable topography (hills dissected by steep valleys). However, many unconformities are near-horizontal or gently dipping, and cut across more steeply dipping (or even folded) strata below.

The Dartmoor granite on Figure 1.7 is the easternmost and largest red blob in southwest England. Look at the outcrop of Permian rocks (beige) just to the northeast on Figure 1.7.

■ How does the form of the western boundary of the Permian outcrop differ from that of its eastern boundary?

☐ The eastern boundary with Triassic rocks is quite straight, running nearly north–south. By contrast, the western boundary is very irregular, with long tongues extending westwards. The rocks to the west of the boundary vary: in the south, they are Devonian; further north they are Carboniferous, and towards the north Devon coast, there are Devonian rocks to the west once more.

■ Which of these two boundaries shows characteristics of an unconformity on this map?

☐ The western boundary; in fact, this is the base of the Permian outcrop. The irregular trace is reminiscent of the unconformity at the base of the Triassic in the Mendips (Section 10.3.3), suggesting deposition of sediments across an irregular, eroded surface. More importantly, the boundary cuts across (truncates) stratigraphic boundaries between older units (Carboniferous and Devonian).

Figure 11.3 Early Permian conglomerates.

At first glance, Permian rocks overlying Carboniferous strata could be a conformable relationship, but the fact that those same Permian rocks also overlie Devonian strata confirms the unconformity. In fact, the base of the Permian throughout Britain is marked by a major unconformity, related to erosion of rocks deformed and uplifted during a mountain-building event (or **orogeny**), the **Variscan Orogeny**, that culminated in the Late Carboniferous. Britain lay largely to the north of the main mountain belt, but east–west striking folds (including the Mendips anticline) and faults associated with the Variscan event occur across southwest England, South Wales, and southern Ireland. On the Bedrock UK Map (S), there are several locations where basal Permian sediments demonstrably overlie older rocks unconformably: near Oswestry at SJ (33) 2826 and 2722; east of Leeds at SE (44) 4232; west of Kirkby Stephen at NY (35) 7410; at several points along the western boundary of the Cadeby and Brotherton formations (P2) between Caldwell (NZ (45) 1614) and the top of the sheet. The latter boundary has the characteristic irregular, indented form of an unconformity, suggesting it is a near-horizontal surface following the topographic contours. There are even isolated outcrops of unconformable Permo-Triassic sediments at several places on the Bedrock UK Map (N), including on Skye. Most of these sediments were deposited when Britain lay near the centre of an arid continent, so that erosion of the continental uplands was dominant and the sediments preserved are mainly locally derived conglomerates and sandstones (Figure 11.3).

Find Hawick (NT (36) 5115) on the Bedrock UK Map (N) and examine the boundary just to the east between the Devonian (D3) and Silurian (S1) strata.

The Devonian rocks here are mainly conglomerates, with some coarse sandstones and finer-grained sediments (Figure 11.4). The conglomerate pebbles are mostly derived from the underlying Silurian sandstones.

■   Would you describe the boundary as straight, or irregular and indented?

□   It is irregular and indented, typical of a sub-horizontal unconformity.

Following the boundary north, there are long tongues of older Devonian rocks (D1) north of Earlston (NT (36) 5738) and north of Polwarth (NT (36) 7550), and the surface at the base of the Devonian cuts across the boundary between the Hawick and Gala Groups (both S1; paler and darker purple, respectively). Contrast the sinuous nature of the basal Devonian unconformity in this area with the straight or gently curved contact between the Hawick and Gala Group rocks running southwest from the Devonian 'tongue' north of Earlston. This contact is depicted by a bolder line than a simple stratigraphic boundary, because it is a fault. Table 11.1 summarises some ways to distinguish between faults and unconformities on geological maps.

Figure 11.4   Early Devonian conglomerates, East Lothian, Scotland. Reproduced with the permission of the British Geological Survey © NERC. All rights Reserved.

Table 11.1   Differences between faults and unconformities on geological maps.

Criterion	Unconformity	Fault
map ornament	lines in general the same weight and colour as normal geological (i.e. stratigraphic) boundaries	lines typically heavier than other geological boundaries; may be ornamented (e.g. tick marks on downthrown side; triangles on thrusts)
index or key	marked as gap or break in vertical section, in some cases with wavy line. May be labelled 'unconformity'	different fault line ornaments shown in key
form of line	commonly irregular, indented and curving, because most have gentle dips	many straight or gently curved (due to moderate or steep dips), but many low-angle thrusts have irregular traces on maps
ages of strata across low-angle surface	low-angle unconformity surfaces have younger beds overlying older beds	most low-angle thrust faults place older strata on top of younger rocks, but the reverse is true for (uncommon) low-angle normal faults
boundaries of older strata truncated	marked truncation is typical of angular unconformities	truncation less common, except within mountain belts
dips of juxtaposed strata	beds above angular unconformity have different (usually gentler) dips to those below the unconformity surface	dips may vary across some faults, but are often similar in strata on both sides, especially outside complex mountain belts

Other outcrops of Devonian rocks occur patchily throughout Scotland and Northern Ireland, overlying a variety of older rocks from the Lower Palaeozoic to the Neoproterozoic. The main outcrops on Figure 1.7 occur in the Orkney and Shetland Isles, around the Moray Firth in northern Scotland, and in the Midland Valley of Scotland, both northwest and southwest of Edinburgh. These Devonian rocks, like many of the basal Permian or Triassic rocks overlying the Variscan unconformity in England, are coarse sandstones or conglomerates of a rich red colour, which are typical of sediments laid down in an arid continental environment (Figures 11.3 and 11.4). In fact, the Devonian and Permian/Triassic sandstone units, originally known as the Old Red Sandstone and New Red Sandstone, respectively, were each derived from rapid erosion of a nearby, newly formed major mountain belt. The Devonian sandstones represent debris eroded from mountains formed by the **Caledonian Orogeny**; the Scottish Highlands are the remnants of those mountains. Numerous other unconformities exist in Britain on a regional or local scale. However, the Devonian and Permian unconformities are very widespread and represent substantial gaps in the stratigraphy, reflecting major tectonic events in the geological history of the region.

11.2.4 Faults

Only a few faults on the Bedrock UK Map extend for over 50 km. One of these, the Highland Boundary Fault (Figure 11.5), marks the northern boundary of the large Devonian outcrop northwest of Edinburgh, visible on Figure 1.7. Despite the substantial time gap between the rocks to the north (Neoproterozoic Dalradian metamorphosed sediments) and those to the south (Devonian), the almost straight trace of this line marks it out as a fault rather than an unconformity. On the Bedrock UK Map (N), this major fault runs continuously from Helensburgh (NS (26) 2983) to Stonehaven (NO (37) 8786). The southern boundary of the Midland Valley is marked by another major fault, the Southern Upland Fault, which runs from Ballantrae (NX (25) 0882) to Dunbar (NT (36) 6879).

Figure 11.5 The Highland Boundary Fault exposed at Garron Point, near Stonehaven. Neoproterozoic Dalradian schists to the north are separated from Ordovician basaltic lavas and Early Devonian conglomerates to the south. The fault is a zone marked by orange streaks in this photograph.

The Great Glen Fault (Figure 11.6), which runs southwest from Inverness (NH (28) 6445) to the Isle of Mull (NM (17)), cuts rocks of the Moine Supergroup (X1–3). This is a strike-slip fault (Figure 10.22c): opposing half-arrows either side of the fault at Inverness (NH (28) 6748) indicate that rocks on the northwestern side have moved southwest relative to those on the southeastern side.

There are also examples of thrust faults on the Bedrock UK Map (N), the largest of which runs up the coastal strip of northwest Scotland from Aird of Sleat on Skye (NG (18) 5900) to Whiten Head (NC (29) 5268) on the north coast. This is the Moine Thrust (labelled MT at intervals), referred to in Question 11.1. The rocks of the Moine Supergroup (X1, yellow) have been thrust northwestwards over the *younger* Cambrian and Ordovician sediments (E1–E3). Along the northern segment of this fault, an olive-green unit labelled simply 'F' represents rocks formed by intense deformation within this fault zone. Another major thrust, the Outer Isles Thrust, snakes down the eastern coast of the Outer Hebrides from Tolastadh Ur (NB (19) 5449) to south of Barra (NL (07) 6590), and is also adorned with extensive outcrops of fault zone rocks (F). Both thrust faults are ornamented on the map with triangles along the fault line, with their apices pointing into the rocks that overlie the fault plane. Their sinuous traces indicate shallower dips than most other faults on the Bedrock UK Map. All these major Scottish faults were originally formed during the Caledonian Orogeny.

- ■ Where would you expect to find thrust faults on the Bedrock UK Map (S)? (Hint: Thrust faults are often associated with folding in orogenic belts.)

- ☐ Where there are Variscan-age folds, i.e. in South Wales and southwest England, including the Mendips area.

The thrust faults in these areas are also ornamented with triangles, but the majority of faults on the Bedrock UK Map (S) are normal faults.

- ■ On the Bedrock UK Map (S), look at the part of the long fault that runs northeast to southwest through grid square SJ (33) 50, in two parallel strands. (Confine your attention to the southwestern part of this 10 km square.) To what geological Period do the rocks (a) to the northwest and (b) to the southeast of the fault belong?

- ☐ (a) Rocks of the Carboniferous Period (C8) lie to the northwest; (b) rocks of the Ordovician Period (O1, O4) lie to the southeast.

The difference in age of these two sets of rocks is more than 100 million years; there has been a major movement on this fault to bring the much older rocks in contact with the younger ones. This fault is the Church Stretton Fault, named after the town at SO (32) 4593, and it is motion on this fault system that has uplifted the Neoproterozoic rocks of the Longmynd (Figure 11.1e) to the surface.

11.2.5 Dykes and sills

You may remember (Section 1.4) the regular pattern of linear, dark-green dykes on the Bedrock UK Map (N) radiating from the igneous centres of Skye (NG (18)) and Mull (NM (17)) (visible on these islands as roughly circular features composed mainly of dark-green and dark-pink blobs labelled *G*). Such a pattern is called a **dyke swarm**. Some of the dykes can be traced southeastwards into northern England. One of these dykes runs from NY (35) 4050 near Dalston through the village of Armathwaite (NY (35) 5047) in

Figure 11.6 Aerial view looking northeastwards along the Great Glen Fault zone towards Loch Lochy. This wide zone of crushed rock has been preferentially eroded by glaciers to produce a deep valley. Reproduced with the permission of the British Geological Survey © NERC. All rights Reserved.

northern Cumbria (not marked on the Bedrock UK Map), and its continuation can be traced (patchily) across the North York Moors, almost to the east coast.

■ What can you deduce about the age of the Armathwaite–Cleveland Dyke from the rocks it cuts through?

☐ The dyke cuts boundaries between Permian and Triassic rocks, both to the southeast and to the northwest of Armathwaite, so it is at least younger than these rocks. However, further east it cuts boundaries between Early (J1) and Middle (J2–3) Jurassic rocks, so it must post-date these units. Its maximum age must be rather less than 200 million years (the base of the Jurassic in the Index and Explanation of the Bedrock UK Map (N)).

In fact, the dyke swarm is Palaeogene in age (some are labelled *G*). The youngest sedimentary rocks that the dykes cut on the UK Bedrock Map (N), on the Antrim coast of Northern Ireland, are Cretaceous White Chalk (K6, pale green) (e.g. at Downhill ((24) 7436) and Ballyvoy ((34) 1541)). (Note: These grid references refer to the Irish National Grid, marked on the Bedrock UK Map (N)). The dykes also cut earlier Palaeogene basalts (pale pink, *G*) in Northern Ireland, Skye and Mull, so they are certainly younger than 65 million years. This last example serves to illustrate the kind of detail that may be extracted from geological maps. As a further confirmation of the age of the Palaeogene basaltic lavas, Figure 11.7 shows thick flows of these lavas overlying the White Chalk in Antrim.

Figure 11.7   Palaeogene basalts overlying White Chalk at Garron Point, Northern Ireland, southeast of Ballyvoy. Reproduced with the permission of the British Geological Survey © NERC. All rights Reserved.

■ All the Palaeogene dykes on the Bedrock UK Map are shown as straight, or very gently curved, lines. What does this indicate about their dips?

□ It suggests that the dykes are steeply dipping (just as steep faults have straight or gently curved traces). In fact, most dykes are subvertical, and represent magma intruded up steep fractures (Section 6.3).

■ The Armathwaite–Cleveland Dyke reaches its maximum thickness of about 25 m near the exposure shown in Figure 11.1a. If a line representing the dyke were drawn to scale on the Bedrock UK Map, what would its maximum thickness be?

□ The Bedrock UK Map has a scale of 1 : 625 000, so the line would be: $25/625\ 000 = 4 \times 10^{-5}$ m thick (or 0.04 mm) – barely visible at all.

Most dykes are only a few metres thick, so they are represented schematically on all but the largest-scale maps of very local areas, with their thickness greatly exaggerated and constant along their length.

Now look at the Bedrock UK Map (N) and find Castle Carrock (NY (35) 5456). A little to the east of Castle Carrock is a Late Carboniferous to earliest Permian intrusion, depicted as a sinuous beige line and labelled *CP*. Like the Armathwaite–Cleveland Dyke, this sheet-like intrusion is shown as discontinuous segments, but you can trace it southeast nearly all the way to Brough (NY (35) 8015). It is intruded into flat-lying Carboniferous sediments.

■ What does the outcrop of this intrusion on the Bedrock UK Map indicate about its dip?

□ The sinuous trace in itself implies that the intrusion follows the topographic contours, and thus has a horizontal or very gentle dip (like the Moine Thrust). Additional support for this deduction is that the intrusion closely follows the stratigraphic boundaries between three of the flat-lying Carboniferous units (C4, C3 and C1), showing pronounced V-patterns up small valleys.

■ Is this intrusion a dyke or a sill, and why?

□ It is a sill, because it is generally concordant with the strata that it intruded (Section 6.3); a dyke would be discordant, cutting across stratigraphic boundaries.

This particular intrusion, known as the Whin Sill, underlies much of northeast England, with outcrops of its resistant igneous rock forming several well-known landscape features. You can trace it northeast from Castle Carrock, from Greenhead (NY (35) 6767) right across to the east coast at Craster (NU (46) 2720), and further up the coast it forms the crags on which Bamburgh Castle (NU (46) 1836) was built. East of Greenhead, the resistant sill forms prominent crags (Figure 11.8) that provide the foundation for a substantial section of Hadrian's Wall.

Figure 11.8   The Whin Sill near Haltwhistle forms resistant crags facing north, which the Romans exploited as the foundation for a defensive wall built across northern England during the reign of the emperor Hadrian (Hadrian's Wall). Reproduced with the permission of the British Geological Survey © NERC. All rights Reserved.

Activity 11.1   The overall geological structure of Britain

In this activity, you will produce a simplified map of the major geological boundaries and structures of Britain.

11.3   Summary of Chapter 11

1   The smallest sedimentary unit is the bed. Progressively larger divisions of strata are known as members, formations and groups.

2   Geological cross-sections are interpretations of the subsurface geology, based on surface information, borehole data, and geophysical exploration.

3   The southern and eastern parts of Britain are characterised by gently dipping, mainly Mesozoic strata, with some broad anticlines and synclines.

4   Two major unconformities are developed across much of Britain. They represent breaks in stratigraphy, due to a cessation of deposition and/or uplift and erosion of mountain belts that were formed during the Caledonian and Variscan Orogenies.

5   Several major faults, running for many tens of kilometres, extend across parts of Britain. Some have long histories, and separate very different bodies of crust. Major thrusts occur in the far northwest of Scotland, South Wales and southwest England.

6   The most prominent dyke swarm on the Bedrock UK Map is Palaeogene in age. Most of the near-vertical dykes radiate from igneous centres in the Western Isles of Scotland (Skye, Mull and Rum). Gently-dipping sills are less common; one important example is the Whin Sill of Late

Carboniferous–Early Permian age that underlies much of northeast England.

11.4 Objectives for Chapter 11

Now you have completed this chapter, you should be able to:

11.1 Understand the basic divisions of sedimentary strata and appreciate how these relate to the lithostratigraphic index of the Bedrock UK Map.

11.2 Interpret the broad patterns of gently dipping and folded Mesozoic strata in lowland Britain using the Bedrock UK Map.

11.3 Trace and identify major unconformities from their map relationships.

11.4 Recognise major fault structures and simple igneous intrusions such as dykes and plutons from their outcrop pattern on a geological map, and use simple cross-cutting relationships to deduce their maximum and minimum ages.

11.5 Deduce whether features such as faults, sheet-like igneous intrusions, or unconformity surfaces are gently or steeply dipping from their form on a geological map.

Now try the following questions to test your understanding of Chapter 11.

Question 11.3

Look at the distribution of thrust faults (black lines ornamented with black triangles) on the Bedrock UK Map (S).

(a) State the four main areas in which these faults occur on this sheet.
(b) Are these areas characterised by simple or complex outcrop patterns when compared with much of the South sheet?
(c) Are large igneous intrusions common in these areas? If so, what are their ages?

Question 11.4

Examine the north–south fault lying between Birmingham and Coventry that passes near Meriden (SP (42) 2483) on the Bedrock UK Map (S).

(a) What strata are shown to the west of the fault?
(b) What strata are shown to the east of the fault?
(c) If this is a normal fault, which is the downthrown side?

Chapter 12   Reading geological history from maps

12.1   Introduction

Although a geological map is primarily a representation of rock outcrop patterns, most geological maps contain much more information than this. Many include information on the structure of the rocks, so that two-dimensional cross-sections can be constructed, enabling the geologist to make three-dimensional interpretations of the subsurface geology. Digital maps within a GIS (Section 1.3.4) may have a wealth of additional information attached to specific locations, features, or rock units, which the user can easily access and analyse. All geological maps provide interpretative tools in the form of special symbols and colours that can help the user to determine the geological history of the region. The approach to extracting information illustrated in the following sections provides a general methodology that you can use to help you understand more complicated geological maps.

You have already learnt how geology relates to topography, how characteristic patterns are produced by horizontal, dipping and folded strata on geological maps, and how to work out the relative motion of strata across faults. The objective of this chapter is to demonstrate how you can use these skills to interpret any geological map, compiling a geological history that outlines the sequence and pattern of rock formation or deposition, faulting and erosion.

12.2   Components of a geological map

12.2.1   Geographical information

With any map, especially an extract of a larger map, it pays first to locate the area in a wider geographical context. Some map sheets include small maps in the margin showing the position of the map relative to neighbouring sheets, or to a larger region. In the absence of latitude and longitude information, the map may have to be located using the national grid for that particular country (these grid lines are typically printed in grey, or a similar unobtrusive colour). 1 : 50 000 BGS map sheets are outlined in red on the Bedrock UK Map, and numbered. The nature of the base map is important. When was it surveyed? This information is commonly noted in the margin. Some maps (e.g. pre-1970s UK, current US maps) may use imperial measures, with contour intervals in feet, not metres, and distances in miles.

12.2.2   General layout of geological maps

Many geological maps typically comprise three basic components (Figure 12.1):

- the map itself
- a cross-section through the area's geology, usually printed below the map

- other marginal information, such as a geological column and a key to the map symbols and colours.

Some maps include brief geological notes; many BGS maps at different scales have separate booklets explaining the geology in some detail. When working with any geological sheet, you should first look at the marginal information (i.e. the key and cross-section), as it will help you use and interpret the map and, ultimately, reconstruct the geological history of the area.

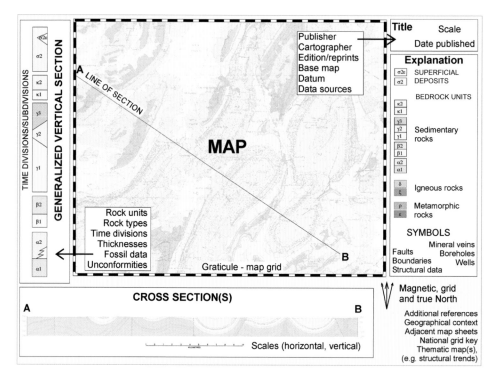

Figure 12.1 Diagram of a typical layout for a geological map sheet, showing the main components schematically. Annotations indicate other supporting information or graphic elements that may be included.

Many maps record the date of publication, subsequent editions and reprints, and details of the topographic base map, including the deviation of magnetic north from grid north at that time. Other sources of data may also be referenced. Such information can be useful because geological interpretations change with time, influencing different generations of cartographers.

12.2.3   Explanation of geological symbols and colours

Every geological map should include a guide to the colours that represent either bedrock ('solid') or superficial ('drift') units – or, in some cases, both. This information tells us the nature and age of the rocks in the mapped area. Deposits of Quaternary sediments known collectively as drift (Section 1.3.3) are generally shown above the bedrock units in the key. Each of the coloured boxes in the key represents a mapped stratigraphic unit, with the youngest at the top and progressively older ones below, while igneous and metamorphic rocks are generally separated out from the sedimentary strata. As many drift deposits are patchily distributed, their relative ages cannot always be precisely determined, so the drift column might not be in strict stratigraphic order. Colours for rock types may follow a convention, so that they can be correlated between different map sheets. However, maps of smaller areas than, say, the Bedrock UK Map show greater geological detail, so more rock units can be identified and a wider range of colours is required to present detailed stratigraphic information. A letter and/or number code assigned to each mapped unit aids identification. However, these codes and colour conventions for strata change over time, as do interpretations of stratigraphy, so maps of different publication dates may be difficult to compare. Codes may include information on the age of the strata (e.g. a letter denoting a Period), or may simply be an abbreviation of the unit (e.g. MMG for Mercia Mudstone Group).

Typically below the explanation of geological units, there is a key to the symbols that describe the direction and amount of dip of the strata. Two common examples are:

- a long strike bar with a tick marking the direction of dip (see Figure 10.8)
- an arrow pointing in the direction of dip (see Figure 10.8).

In each case, the dip angle in degrees is given next to the symbol. Figure 10.8 relates these symbols to a block diagram of dipping strata. Horizontal beds are often indicated by a cross (+).

The key also shows the different symbols used to represent geological boundaries. A solid line is used where a geological boundary can be determined with certainty; for instance, where stratigraphic boundaries are exposed in quarries, in cliff faces, or otherwise obviously expressed in the topography. Dashed lines are used for geological boundaries that cannot be accurately positioned on the ground due to poor exposure. Faults (Section 10.3.4) are typically marked as a heavy broken line, or a solid heavy line where they are exposed. Most importantly, the downthrown side may be indicated by a small tick mark.

Other features, such as boreholes, wells and mineral veins, may also be marked with symbols, but the information on paper maps is limited by the need to maintain clarity. Digital maps stored in a GIS are not subject to the same constraints. All the different elements of the geology mentioned above, and many more, can be stored in different data 'layers', allowing any combination of bedrock, superficial and artificial deposits – and other data – to be viewed, queried, and plotted independently using GIS software. For instance, full borehole records can be stored, which is in contrast to the scant annotations next to the borehole symbols on some maps. Boreholes provide crucial extra information on the stratigraphy at depth, allowing geologists to construct vertical and horizontal cross-sections with more confidence, and interpret the subsurface structure.

12.2.4   The generalised vertical section

On first glance, you may think that the generalised vertical section to the left of the map simply repeats information given in the explanation of geological symbols and colours. However, the explanation is only designed to tell you which rock types occur at the surface; it does not give other crucial geological information, such as the relative thicknesses of the beds, how individual beds may vary in thickness, whether there are gaps in the sedimentary succession, or whether there is information available about the subsurface rocks lying below those exposed within the map area. A generalised vertical section helps answer these questions.

Vertical sections are generally drawn to scale, giving a direct visual guide to the range of thicknesses of the stratigraphic units in this area; these thicknesses may vary appreciably, and some units may pinch out entirely, being represented by a triangular wedge in the column (as on the Bedrock UK Map, Section 11.1.1). Unconformities are represented by gaps, in some cases marked by wavy lines or labelled. The vertical section also provides an opportunity to include brief lithological descriptions, valuable for identifying distinctive 'marker' horizons or fossiliferous strata. In addition, a sedimentary unit may change its lithological character laterally along its outcrop as a result of different depositional conditions having existed at the same time in different places. For instance, limestone may be deposited offshore at the same time as siltstones accumulate near a river mouth. Since the resulting different lithologies are of the same age, they can be correlated (Section 1.4) and so are shown occupying a similar position in the vertical section.

12.2.5   The geological cross-section

The geological cross-section represents a vertical slice along a line drawn across the map, cutting down through the topographic surface into underlying rock strata. It is an interpretation of the subsurface geology deduced from the distribution of rock units mapped at the surface, sometimes augmented with evidence from other sources such as boreholes or geophysical surveys. The cross-section and the map, together, help geologists visualise the three-dimensional relationships of the rocks within a particular area. Note that section lines may have several segments trending on different bearings. Some maps have more than one cross-section.

If the map scale is large enough for the beds to be easily represented on the section at true scale, vertical exaggeration can be avoided, so that the true values of ground surface slopes, strata dip angles and stratigraphic thicknesses are preserved. You should check for vertical exaggeration by comparing the vertical and horizontal scales before investigating the section in detail.

Box 12.1 provides a useful checklist of the types of geographical and geological information that should be examined when you first look at a geological map. The section that follows examines other clues that can be used to paint a more complete picture of the geological history.

Box 12.1 Checklist: your first look at a new geological map

Many modern geological maps use a similar format to BGS sheets, though details differ in different countries. Here are some guidelines to help you tackle such maps when you first look at them.

1 Locate the sheet on a small-scale map of the country, such as the Bedrock UK Map (the edges of all 1 : 50 000 maps are overprinted in red on the Bedrock UK Map, together with the sheet numbers).

2 Determine the scale of the map (often marked near the top of the sheet).

3 From the Geographical Information for the base map (usually printed in grey on BGS maps), determine:

   (a) the nature of the grid and the spacing of grid lines

   (b) whether the contours are in feet or metres, and what the contour interval is

   (c) when the geographical survey was carried out (i.e. whether or not it is relatively modern).

4 From the Geological Information (usually printed in black on BGS maps):

   (a) determine whether the map depicts bedrock ('solid') and/or superficial deposits ('drift')

   (b) from the key (often called 'explanation of geological symbols and colours', or 'index'), determine which rock types and ages are present from the stratigraphic column. Solid and drift information is usually separate. Check whether there are any special symbols given, such as overturned or vertical strata, or thrusts

   (c) from the generalised vertical section(s), determine what variations in thicknesses of strata occur within the area of the map. Note the scale(s) of these vertical columns and the particular area to which a specific column applies. Note especially the presence of unconformities (breaks in the column, or a wavy line), and if wedging out of strata occurs

   (d) from the cross-section(s), determine what, if any, vertical exaggeration has been applied. Locate where the line(s) of section cross(es) the map.

Activity 12.1   Introduction to the Cheddar map sheet

This activity will help you assimilate key background information on the geological map of the Cheddar area.

12.3   Critical clues to geological histories

12.3.1   Stratigraphic successions

The Principle of Superposition (Section 1.1) dictates that the age of sedimentary rocks in an undisturbed, conformable succession increases downwards (i.e. the youngest strata lie at the top). Hence, the earliest event that can be easily deduced from many geological maps is the deposition of the oldest sediment. This information is readily available from either the index (stratigraphic column) or the generalised vertical section (if present). If the strata above are conformable, overlying the deepest stratum with no breaks, then this suggests that the sediments were laid down one after the other in sequence. Notes on the lithology of specific strata (e.g. on the generalised vertical section) may then reveal more information on the changing environments in which the original sediments were deposited.

12.3.2   Unconformities: breaks in the rock record

An unconformity represents a gap in the stratigraphy, which must mean either a hiatus (break) in sedimentation, and/or the removal of some strata by uplift and erosion. It may not be possible to determine which of these scenarios occurred from the map alone without more detailed knowledge of, for instance, what sort of pebbles are found in a basal conglomerate resting on the unconformity. However, it is worth checking the generalised vertical section for specific information such as this. The time gap represented by an unconformity can be determined from the age difference between the strata above and below it, and the form of the surface can give clues to the processes that formed the unconformity. An *angular unconformity*, like the one at Vallis Vale (Figure 10.20), confirms that the older rocks must have been deformed (tilted or folded), then uplifted and eroded, before the younger sediments were deposited. There may be clues in the vertical section to the nature of the unconformity; for instance, a surface may be described as weathered, implying it was exposed subaerially – perhaps as a result of uplift – before sediments were deposited on top. Some unconformities are not simple, planar surfaces, but rugged and irregular, reflecting the actively eroding landscape on which younger strata were then laid down. A classic example is the unconformity in northwest Scotland between the eroded Archean Lewisian Gneiss Complex (A1–3 on the Bedrock UK Map (N) and the overlying Proterozoic 'Torridonian' sandstones and conglomerates (X1 and Y3). The coarse grain size and reddish colour of the Torridonian sandstones, features likely to be recorded on the vertical section of a geological map, are consistent with subaerial deposition, so the Lewisian gneisses must have been uplifted and then eroded at the time of the unconformity. Around Loch Maree (grid square NG (18) 97), this ancient **buried topography** has a relief of up to 600 m; when an ancient landscape such as this is uplifted and exposed by more recent uplift, it is described as an **exhumed topography**. The unconformity between the Carboniferous and Triassic conglomerate in the Mendip area (Section 10.3.3) is another example of exhumed topography.

12.3.3 Cross-cutting relationships: faults and intrusions

Wherever geological boundaries on a geological map are sharply truncated, for instance by the trace of an angular unconformity, this provides critical evidence for the relative timing of the two features. Truncations show up as conspicuous 'T-junctions', and are worth seeking out when you first look at a geological map. Such cross-cutting relationships are extremely useful in slotting different geological events into a relative timeline when reconstructing the history of an area, and can be applied to many different features. The general rule is:

> A feature that cuts across another feature is younger than the one it cuts across.

An everyday example is provided by a road surface in a town that has been repeatedly dug up for work on underground services, patched, widened, modified and painted. The relative age of all the works can be determined from which features (e.g. tarmac strips and white lines) cut across others. The feature cross-cutting everything else (say, the new pedestrian crossing) must be the youngest.

The pattern of a cross-cutting igneous dyke on a geological map is similar to a track of gleaming tarmac marking the course of a new underground cable. The dyke must be younger than the youngest rock (or other feature) it cuts across, since the older rock or feature must have been present when the dyke was intruded. Even then, the dyke may be *much* younger than the youngest rock it cuts across. As you saw for the Armathwaite–Cleveland Dyke in Section 11.2.5, careful inspection along the dyke's length is needed to find the youngest rock or feature that it cuts, and it may be possible to correlate the intrusion with similar ones that cut different (perhaps younger) rocks.

It is generally difficult to demonstrate that younger sediments cross-cut (i.e. overlie) older intrusions on a map, but the Bedrock UK Map (N) provides a useful illustration of the principle in northwest Scotland. All along the northwest coast, west of the Moine Thrust (Section 11.2.4), lie the oldest rocks in Britain: the Lewisian Gneisses (A1, pink). These ancient gneisses are cross-cut by Palaeoproterozoic dykes (z, green), striking mainly NW–SE. Although their age is given in the map index, the map itself indicates that these dykes are terminated abruptly by the boundary with the Cambrian Ardvreck Group sediments (E1–2, pale green), for example, at NC (29) 2216. None of these dykes crosses this boundary, because it is a younger (Cambrian) unconformity where the Ardvreck Group sediments overlie both Lewisian Gneiss and Torridonian Group sediments (X1). So the dykes must be older than Cambrian. In fact, their age can be pinpointed more precisely using similar relationships with Torridon Group sediments (X1) at NH (28) 0476, and Stoer Group sediments (Y3) at NC (29) 0429. These two cross-cutting relationships indicate that the dykes must be older than those Neoproterozoic and Mesoproterozoic sediments. The age of faults can also be bracketed by observing the youngest rocks or features cut by the fault and the oldest features that cut across the fault. Consider all types of feature: plutons, dykes, stratigraphic boundaries, and other faults. The process is iterative: bracketing the age of a long fault, for example, may place good age constraints on other features along its length. On the Bedrock UK Map (N), locate the fault that runs northeast from NX (25) 4756 (near Carsluith) to NT (36) 5444 (about 8 km northeast of Galashiels).

■ What is the oldest feature that cuts across the fault?

☐ Two outcrops of unit P1 (sandstones of Early Permian age) overlie and obscure the fault northwest of Dumfries (NX (25) 9776) and south of Moffat (NT (36) 0906). However, the northeast end of the fault is clearly truncated by an irregular boundary between Silurian Hawick Group strata (S1) and overlying Lower Devonian rocks (D1). Hence, the oldest feature that cuts the fault is this boundary, the unconformity you studied in Section 11.2.3.

■ What is the youngest feature cut by the fault?

☐ The youngest stratigraphic unit cut by the fault is the Silurian Hawick Group (S1), which is somewhat younger than 444 Ma. (A small Palaeogene dyke (G) west of Dumfries appears to be cut and offset by the fault, which would imply the fault is younger than Palaeogene. However, you know the fault *must* be older than Early Devonian from the evidence above, and other Palaeogene dykes clearly cross-cut the fault northeast of Moffat. This one Palaeogene dyke probably intruded along the fault for a short distance, producing an apparent offset.)

Recent research (2008) suggests that this offset dyke is one of several segments marking the continuation of the Armathwaite-Cleveland dyke (section 11.2.5).

This evidence brackets the age of the fault between that of the Hawick Group (Silurian) and the D1 unit (Early Devonian). Dykes of similar age (SD) occur in two places close to the fault. One just east of Moffat appears to be truncated at the fault, while the other (about 9 km northeast of Carsluith) appears to cut obliquely across the fault. These relationships are rather ambiguous, possibly because these dykes are a very similar age to the fault (around the Silurian–Devonian boundary).

12.3.4 Other events: deformation and metamorphism

The association of faults with folds in rocks that are overlain by an unconformity is typical of an area that has experienced a major mountain-building event. Careful examination of the relationships between these geological features in an area such as the Mendips can bracket the age of such an event quite closely. However, this is not always the case! Some evidence for events in a geological history is much more sparse. Metamorphic rocks are commonly formed and exhumed during mountain-building events, but there are none exposed on Figure 10.15 in the Mendip area. Such rocks are typically also deformed (by folding and/or faulting), and hence determining the ages of the folds or faults may help to constrain the timing of metamorphism (though metamorphic rocks could also be affected by folding or faulting events long after the metamorphic event). The age of metamorphic rocks given in an index may be the time they were deposited as sediments, not the time of metamorphism. For example, the Dalradian Supergroup (X5–X8) on the Bedrock UK Map (N) was originally a pile of sediments laid down in the Neoproterozoic–Cambrian, but these sediments were not metamorphosed until ~ 470 Ma, during the Ordovician. Deducing this from the map is not easy. However, in several places the deformed Dalradian strata are overlain (and hence truncated on the map) by unmetamorphosed Early Devonian sediments (for instance, around Tomintoul, NJ (38) 1719), so metamorphism of the Dalradian rocks must have occurred before then, otherwise those sediments would also have been metamorphosed. In fact, several Silurian–Devonian granite intrusions (*SD*) in the same general area also cross-cut the metamorphosed Dalradian rocks (e.g. east of Knockandhu at NJ (38) 2624 and west of Lochnagar at NO (37) 1886), implying that the metamorphism must be older than these granites.

■   What information is needed to be sure that these intrusions do indeed post-date metamorphism of the Dalradian?

☐   Evidence that the granites are not deformed or metamorphosed themselves. If they were, then the metamorphism would be younger than them. (In fact, these granites are unaffected by the metamorphism or deformation, which is an important constraint on their age.)

The timing of deformation events may be constrained by observing the relationships of folds and faults on a map. Clearly, the deformation must post-date the deposition of any strata it affects. The Mendip anticline, for example, must have formed after the Asbian–Brigantian Stage of the Carboniferous, during which the Hotwells Limestone was laid down. Similarly, if unfolded rocks overlie folded rocks, the folding event must pre-date the depositional age of the unfolded, younger strata.

12.3.5 From geological map to geological history: a summary

Box 12.2 summarises the strategies you can use to reconstruct the geological history of any area with relatively complex geology, such as the Mendips or northwest Scotland.

Box 12.2   Compiling a geological history

1   Find the oldest rocks on the map. These could be igneous, metamorphic or sedimentary. The first identifiable event in the geological history could therefore be either crystallisation of an igneous rock or the deposition of sediments that may or may not have been metamorphosed later.

2   Are there unconformities present? If so, they are normally indicated in the stratigraphic column on the map. Consider the oldest unconformity first.

> Steps 3–6 assume that an unconformity is present; if there is no unconformity, simply record the sequence of strata from oldest (lowermost) to youngest (uppermost), and then proceed to step 8.

3   Do the beds below the unconformity show any evidence of the following: (a) folding; (b) faulting; (c) igneous intrusions; (d) metamorphism?

4   Is there evidence that these events did not affect rocks above the unconformity? If so, this confirms that the events occurred before the younger strata were deposited. For example, a fault may cut older strata but disappear at the unconformity. If more than one of (a)–(d) has occurred, work out the order in which they happened by determining which features (younger) cut across the others (older).

5   The unconformity itself indicates a time gap unrepresented by strata, usually because of a period of uplift above sea level and erosion.

6   Subsequently, the series of beds above the unconformity were deposited.

7   Is there another, later, unconformity present? If so, repeat steps 3 to 6 until the latest series of sediments is reached.

8   Have the most recent sediments been: (a) folded; (b) faulted; (c) intruded; (d) metamorphosed?

9   Is there evidence for tilting and erosion since the area was finally uplifted to form land?

10 Is there evidence of any Quaternary glacial activity, such as glacial drift material?

11 Is there evidence of more recent sediments, such as river terrace deposits?

Arguably, the most recent chapter in the geological history of an area would be the impact (if any) of humans – for instance by mining, quarrying, landfill, or other large-scale engineering operations.

Activity 12.2 Geological history of the Cheddar area

In this activity, you will deduce the geological history of part of the Cheddar area.

12.4   Summary of Chapter 12

1   Geological map sheets typically include marginal information that helps the reader interpret the geological features shown on the map.

2   Geographical information, such as location on a National Grid, places map sheets in a wider geographical context.

3   Marginal information generally includes an explanation of the geological colours and symbols used on the map, allowing recognition of geological units, faults, folds and features such as boreholes.

4   Some maps show the distribution of superficial ('drift') deposits in addition to the bedrock geology.

5   Faults and boundaries are marked with solid lines where observed, and dashed or broken lines where they are inferred.

6   Many maps include a generalised vertical section, which provides detailed stratigraphic information such as variations in bed thickness, wedging-out relationships, lithological notes and unconformities.

7   Geological cross-sections are common as marginal additions to geological map sheets, and present interpretations of the subsurface geology along a line marked on the map.

8   Information gleaned from a map sheet on stratigraphic successions, unconformities and cross-cutting relationships of faults and intrusions contributes to reconstructing the geological history of a mapped area.

12.5   Objectives for Chapter 12

Now you have completed this chapter, you should be able to:

12.1 Use the wealth of information on geological map sheets to place an area in a geographical context and interpret the surface geology.

12.2 Use the information provided in cross-sections and borehole records to visualise and interpret the subsurface structure of a mapped area.

12.3 Apply the Principle of Superposition to stratigraphic information in the generalised vertical section to infer the sequence of deposition of sediments in an area.

12.4 Work out the relative timing of geological events such as deposition, metamorphism, igneous activity and deformation using cross-cutting relationships.

12.5 Interpret the geological history of an area containing sedimentary rocks, folded and metamorphosed strata, igneous intrusions, faults and unconformities.

Now try the following question to test your understanding of Chapter 12.

Question 12.1

(a) Which of the following correctly describes the feature labelled 'G3' on the Bedrock UK Map (S) at TG (63) 3802? Briefly justify your answer.

    (i)   a small granite intrusion

    (ii) a Palaeogene inlier

    (iii) an Eocene outlier

(b) Which of the following correctly describes the elongate, dark-blue outcrop on the Bedrock UK Map (S) at TL (52) 4775, southwest of Ely?

    (i)   an outlier of Gault and Upper Greensand Formations

    (ii) a Cretaceous mafic sill

    (iii) a Cretaceous mafic dyke

    (iv) an inlier of Cretaceous mudstone and sandstone

(c) What is the main evidence that the geological boundary running NNW from Norwich (TG (63) 2309) to the Norfolk coast, west of Sheringham (TG (63) 1143), is an unconformity?

(d) Is the Cretaceous (K2–K6) north of the Humber (TA (54) 0025) separated by an unconformity from the rocks below? Give reasons for your answer.

Answers to questions

Question 1.1

You should have concluded that the oldest rocks in Britain (mid Precambrian in age) make up the Outer Hebrides and parts of northwest Scotland, and that the youngest rocks are the Cenozoic clays and sands of the Thames Estuary, and the coastal parts of East Anglia and Hampshire area.

Question 1.2

You should have written down the stratigraphic column for the whole of the Cenozoic, Mesozoic and Palaeozoic, with the exception of the Cambrian Period, which is not encountered along this line. You may also have crossed a small area of Silurian rocks between the Carboniferous and the Devonian in the vicinity of the Scottish border, and the last few kilometres to Edinburgh are on Carboniferous rocks after crossing the oldest rocks of the traverse, namely the Ordovician.

Question 1.3

(a) Metamorphic rocks are almost entirely confined to the Highlands and Islands of Scotland, and northwest Ireland. You may also have discovered small areas in Anglesey and the Lleyn Peninsula in North Wales. There is also a very small patch in South Devon (at Start Point), and another at the southeastern tip of Ireland.

(b) The largest extent of igneous intrusive rocks is in the Highlands of Scotland, so they appear to be associated mainly with metamorphic rocks. There are also igneous intrusions in southern Scotland, northern and southwestern England and various parts of Ireland, with some small occurrences in west Wales. The extrusive igneous rocks show a rather different distribution. They are more extensively associated with sedimentary rocks, but again are concentrated in western and southern Scotland, northern and northwestern England, North Wales and Northern Ireland.

Question 1.4

It is easiest to use the values given for a map with a metric scale (e.g. 1 : 10 000) in Table 1.1 to answer this question. On a 1 : 10 000 map, Uluru is 31 cm long. Because each centimetre on the map represents 10 000 cm on the ground, Uluru is actually $31 \times 10\,000 = 310\,000$ cm long. Since there are 100 000 cm in 1 km, the rock's length in kilometres is

$$\frac{310\,000}{100\,000} = 3.1\,\text{km}.$$

Question 1.5

(a) Salisbury.

(b) Chalk with flints (White Chalk Subgroup).

(c) Mesozoic Era and Cretaceous Period.

(d) Between 146 and 65 million years ago according to the timescale on the Bedrock UK Map, but probably not long before 65 Ma, because the White Chalk (K6) is the uppermost unit in the Cretaceous column.

Question 1.6

(a) Triassic (Unit T2).

(b) Ordovician (Units O1 to O3).

(c) Ordovician (O1–3, perhaps also latest Cambrian), Silurian (S1–3), Devonian (D1), Carboniferous (C1, C2, C3), Permian (P1, P3), Triassic (T2).

Question 1.7

(a) Both areas of rock belong to the Devonian Period and are between 359 and 416 million years old.

(b) London lies on the Palaeogene and Neogene (1.8–65 million years) and Dublin on the Carboniferous (299–359 million years). The maximum possible age difference is about 357 million years if London were on the youngest Neogene beds and Dublin on the oldest Carboniferous.

Question 2.1

(a) Figure 2.23a: tetragonal; Figure 2.23b: monoclinic. Note that while two axes are at 90° to each other, one axis is inclined – hence the term 'monoclinic'; Figure 2.23c: orthorhombic. See Figure 2.24.

(b) The cross-section would be square.

Question 2.2

(a) The pressure is 0.05 MPa.

(b) The triple point at which ice, water and steam coexist is defined by the intersection of the three phase boundaries: ice/water, ice/steam, and water/steam. This corresponds to a temperature of 6 °C and a pressure of 0.03 MPa (Figure 2.3).

Question 2.3

The mineral's hardness is 6. The hardness must be greater than that of window glass (5.5), and less than that of hardened steel (6.5).

Question 3.1

The mineral is isotropic, and hence is likely to belong to the cubic system. (Note, however, that it is also possible to observe an anisotropic crystal (in basal section) that appears to be isotropic, due to its orientation (Section 3.2.5).)

Question 3.2

An anisotropic mineral has two permitted vibration directions. If the crystal is rotated so that one permitted vibration direction is parallel to the polariser direction, then all the light passing through the crystal will vibrate parallel to this direction. The relief seen will depend on the refractive index for this vibration direction. At 90° to this direction, all the light will vibrate parallel to the other permitted vibration direction, and the relief seen will depend on the other principal refractive index for this section.

If there is a large change in relief as the stage is rotated, then the two refractive indices must be very different. The mineral must therefore have very high birefringence, be highly anisotropic, and should display high-order interference colours.

Question 3.3

Diamond has a cubic structure (strong bonds in all directions), and so will be optically isotropic. It is a relatively dense structure (Table 2.1), and so it is expected to have a high refractive index. (The high refractive index of diamond causes the 'fire' of the gemstone.) Diamond crystals would therefore exhibit very high relief in plane-polarised light, and would appear dark in all orientations when viewed between crossed polars.

Graphite has a layer structure with strong bonds within each layer, but weak bonds between successive layers (Figure 2.16b). A large difference would be expected between the refractive index for light vibrating parallel to the layers, and light vibrating perpendicular to the layers. Graphite is therefore predicted to be highly anisotropic, and should show high-order interference colours when viewed between crossed polars. (In fact, graphite usually appears opaque – but when very thin flakes are cut, it has a deep-blue colour.)

Question 4.1

A vertical line through 300 °C on the temperature axis in Figure 4.11 cuts the stishovite/coesite phase boundary at a pressure of 8 GPa. Thus, if a sample of silica were held at 300 °C and at a pressure of 8 GPa or higher, it would transform into stishovite.

Question 4.2

The composition represented by point X is 80% A and 20% B ($A_{0.8}B_{0.2}$). The composition represented by point Y is 20% A, 60% B, and 20% C ($A_{0.2}B_{0.6}C_{0.2}$).

Question 4.3

Quartz has a fully polymerised structure in which each SiO_4 tetrahedron is connected to four other tetrahedra that *share corners* (i.e. each oxygen atom is shared between two tetrahedra). So, although each silicon atom is bonded to four oxygen atoms, it has to share each oxygen atom with another silicon atom. This makes the ratio of silicon to oxygen 1 : 2, and, hence, the chemical formula for quartz is SiO_2.

Question 4.4

Cleavage is caused by differences in the strengths of bonding in different directions, or planes, in the crystal structure. The quartz structure has strong Si–O bonds in all directions, with no preferential directions of weakness. Quartz, therefore, has no cleavage and, when struck with a hammer, a quartz crystal breaks into curved fragments. In contrast, the mica structure (Figure 4.7) has strong bonds within the layer sandwiches and weaker bonds between adjacent sandwiches. This results in distinct planes of weakness and a perfect cleavage between the structural sandwiches.

Question 4.5

Solid solution is developed when a range of chemical compositions is possible in a given crystal structure. Solid solution involves the substitution of one or more ions at specific sites in the crystal structure. For example, olivines can range in composition from pure Mg_2SiO_4 to pure Fe_2SiO_4 – with a continuous spread of compositions in between, with Mg^{2+} substituting for Fe^{2+}, and vice versa. Other examples of solid solution include the plagioclase feldspars (from anorthite, $CaAl_2Si_2O_8$, to albite, $NaAlSi_3O_8$) and the alkali feldspars (from albite, $NaAlSi_3O_8$, to potassium feldspar, $KAlSi_3O_8$) at high temperatures.

Question 6.1

The large crystals would have started crystallising under conditions of slow cooling at a few nucleation centres. At high temperature, long-range diffusion of atoms in the magma is possible and would favour continued crystal growth. After a time, the conditions must have changed rapidly (probably as a result of sudden cooling and/or release of gases). The rapid cooling gave rise to a large number of nucleation centres, and severely restricted the diffusion of atoms, so producing many small crystals.

Question 6.2

They are all fine grained, with randomly oriented, interlocking crystals (this would only be obvious in thin section), and possibly glass, indicating rapid cooling as a result of magma being erupted at the Earth's surface.

Question 6.3

Calcite has a hardness of 3 and so can be scratched with a penknife, whereas quartz has a hardness of 7 and cannot be scratched in this way. In fact, quartz will leave a scratch mark on any mild steel object. Also, calcite will 'fizz' with dilute hydrochloric acid, because calcite is a carbonate that reacts readily with the acid to give off carbon dioxide (see 'acid test' for calcite in the Digital Kit). Quartz does not react with dilute acids.

Question 6.4

(a) The oxides FeO, MgO, CaO and TiO_2 (also Fe_2O_3) are much more abundant in gabbro than granite.

(b) Plagioclase feldspar (Section 4.6.2) and pyroxene (Section 4.4.1), as both have Ca-rich varieties.

(c) Pyroxene and olivine, as they are both ferromagnesian minerals (Section 2.3.2).

Question 6.5

(a) From Table 6.4 and Figure 6.15, a SiO_2 content of 55 wt % corresponds to an intermediate rock.

(b) Figure 6.15 shows quartz is not likely to be a major constituent and that the dominant mineral is plagioclase feldspar of intermediate composition (i.e. it contains roughly equal amounts of Ca-rich and Na-rich components) with lesser amounts of mafic minerals, such as pyroxene, amphibole and biotite.

The volume percentage of plagioclase can be estimated from the spread of the plagioclase field on the vertical scale. Thus, there will be approximately 68% − 5% = 63% plagioclase in this rock (see Figure 13.1). By the same reasoning, you could expect the rock to contain about 32% mafic minerals, made up from about 12% pyroxene, 10% amphibole and 10% biotite. It also contains a small amount (about 5%) of quartz, but not enough to see in hand specimen and not easy to see in thin section.

(c) The rock is a diorite (see also Figure 6.6).

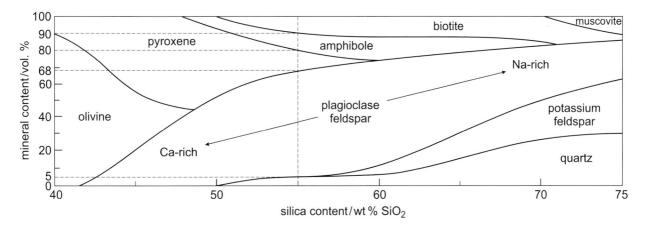

Figure 13.1 Solution for Question 6.5b.

Question 6.6

Both rocks are crystalline and igneous. They contain the same principal minerals: quartz and potassium feldspar (microcline in the granite, orthoclase in the porphyritic rhyolite). As they have similar mineral compositions, they would have crystallised from magmas of similar chemical composition.

The coarse and relatively even-grained (equigranular) texture of the granite is the result of slow cooling, which enabled large crystals to grow. In the porphyritic rhyolite, the large crystals (phenocrysts) would have formed during an initial period of slow cooling at considerable depth beneath the surface, whereas the fine-grained groundmass formed during more rapid cooling at or near the Earth's surface.

Question 6.7

(a) Using in reverse the principle of the method outlined in the answer to Question 6.5b, the medium-grained rock with this mineralogy would be a microdiorite (Figure 13.2).

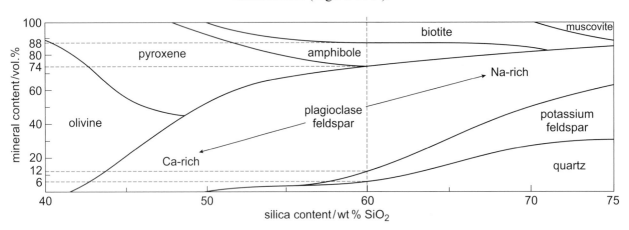

Figure 13.2   Solution for Question 6.7a.

(b) The silica (SiO$_2$) content of such a rock would be approximately 60 wt % (Figure 13.2). [*Comment*: These mineral proportions were chosen to fit exactly the relative proportions shown in Figure 6.15. Be aware, however, that this figure is idealised and in nature there is a degree of variation. For example, another rock could exist with 15% biotite and 10% amphibole, but with the other minerals in the same relative proportions as in the first rock. This second rock would not be an *exact* match to any composition in Figure 6.15, but would have *roughly* the same SiO$_2$ content, and the same name, as the first rock.]

(c) The volcanic equivalent of a microdiorite is andesite and the plutonic equivalent is diorite (see also Table 6.2).

Question 6.8

(a) Both Table 6.4 and Figure 6.15 show that the rock is mafic (48 wt % SiO_2).

(b) By the method outlined in the answer to Question 6.5b, the minerals are likely to be present in the following (approximate) proportions: Ca-rich plagioclase feldspar (42%), pyroxene (100% − 46% = 54%) and olivine (46% − 42% = 4%).

(c) The rock is fine grained, so it is a basalt (Tables 6.2 and 6.4).

Question 6.9

At 44 wt %, the percentage of $FeO + Fe_2O_3 + MgO$ in this rock is very high, much higher than in, for example, basalt (Question 6.8). The percentage of SiO_2 is very low (43 wt %). According to Figure 6.15, it would be an ultramafic igneous rock, containing about 90% of mafic minerals (olivine and pyroxene).

Question 6.10

Table 6.3 indicates there is more than 66 wt % SiO_2 in the chemical analysis of a typical granite, which places it in the felsic category. From Figure 6.15, you can see that granites contain about 20–30% quartz and are rich in plagioclase and potassium feldspar; altogether they contain at least 80% felsic minerals, which again classify them as felsic. (See also Table 6.4.)

Question 7.1

(a) sandy mudstone

(b) calcareous sandstone

(c) muddy limestone or marl.

Question 7.2

(a) quartz, composed entirely of silica, SiO_2

(b) clay minerals, which are aluminosilicates (Section 4.5.2)

(c) calcite (calcium carbonate, $CaCO_3$).

Question 7.3

Muscovite is a felsic mineral that crystallises at relatively low temperatures (Figure 6.6) and is stable at low temperatures so it often survives chemical weathering. It is commonly found in sedimentary rocks, particularly those deposited in water (Section 7.4). Biotite is a mafic mineral that crystallises and is stable at higher temperatures (Figure 6.6) and is less stable than muscovite at lower temperatures, so it is more susceptible to chemical weathering and rarely survives in sedimentary rocks.

Question 7.4

(a) Sediments derived from quartz sandstone would consist entirely of recycled quartz grains. Weathering would break down some or all the cement holding the grains together and the quartz grains (and small sandstone fragments) would be transported away to form new quartz-rich sediments.

(b) Granite would break down chemically to clay minerals formed from the feldspar and biotite, and to iron oxides formed from the biotite. The rock would then crumble to liberate grains of quartz and flakes of muscovite. If chemical weathering does not decompose the feldspars completely, a feldspar-rich sandstone (arkose) might be formed. However, the final end-product of prolonged transport and continued chemical weathering would be silts or clays, and quartz sands.

(c) The weathering of gabbro would produce mainly iron oxides from the olivine and pyroxene, and clay minerals from the plagioclase feldspar.

Question 8.1

The most obvious source of heat is directly from igneous intrusions, but deep burial in the Earth's crust, often associated with tectonic compression and mountain building, also leads to an increase in temperature, along with an increase in pressure.

Question 8.2

In thin section, biotite would probably have a brown colour and be strongly pleochroic in plane-polarised light.

Question 8.3

Phenocrysts are large, well-formed crystals in igneous rocks. They are associated with a two-stage cooling as described in the answer to Question 6.1. As they started to grow early in the cooling history of a magma, there was little else crystallising to hinder crystal growth. A rock containing phenocrysts is described as porphyritic (perhaps confusingly similar to porphyroblastic).

Question 8.4

The two mineral assemblages would be different. Even if both mudstones and basalt were subjected to the same temperature and pressure conditions during metamorphism, the chemical composition of basalt is very different from that of the mudstones. [*Comment*: In fact, at a moderate degree of metamorphism, the mudstones would be metamorphosed into schists, whereas the basalt would be metamorphosed into an amphibolite.]

Question 8.5

The slate is a fine-grained metamorphic rock, whereas the schist is coarse grained and porphyroblastic. Both rocks are of similar composition, but the larger grain size of the schist suggests the metamorphism was for longer and/ or under higher temperature and pressure conditions than for the slate.

Question 8.6

Both of these rocks are porphyroblastic. The matrix of both is probably dominated by quartz and muscovite mica. However, there are also compositional differences: the original sediment from which the pyritic slate was formed must have contained some sulfur to form the pyrite porphyroblasts on metamorphism, whereas the original material of the garnet-bearing schist consisted almost entirely of silicate minerals, some of which recrystallised to form the garnet porphyroblasts. The grain size is also very different, with the pyritic slate formed at lower pressures and temperatures than the garnet mica schist.

Question 8.7

Marble is a crystalline rock without any mineral alignment – one of the main textural criteria for identifying rocks as being of igneous origin. However, this rock is almost entirely made up of calcite crystals (which are softer than quartz and fizz with dilute HCl, Section 4.7.1) with an interlocking granular texture. Clearly, it cannot be a silicate igneous rock, and therefore must be a marble, formed by the metamorphic recrystallisation of limestone.

Question 9.1

The vertical exposure contains a distinct structural feature trending from top right to bottom left. It appears to have much smoother surfaces and a more regular pattern of joints than the rocks on either side, which have irregular surfaces and appear to be structureless. This rock unit thus appears to cut across the structureless rock. It forms a sheet with subparallel sides. This feature could be an igneous dyke, cutting other igneous rocks. Inspection of the rocks to either side would indicate what kind of igneous rocks they are. If the feature is a dyke, the immediately adjacent rocks may well be metamorphosed by the heat of the intrusion, making their identification difficult.

Question 9.2

The rock strata form distinct parallel layers, which appear to be horizontal. Some layers project out and must be harder, and therefore more resistant to erosion, than those between. They could be well-cemented sandstones or limestones. Close inspection would indicate which. They alternate with softer layers that could be mudstones or shales. This sequence suggests that conditions of deposition alternated repeatedly over the area. A search for fossils could provide evidence of the age of these rocks.

Question 10.1

(a) Wytham Hill is formed of Jurassic Corallian limestone (J5).

(b) As mentioned earlier, the Corallian limestone includes moderately resistant limestones that, at this location, have not been eroded as easily as the surrounding rocks (mudstones of the Kellaways and Oxford Clay Formations, J4). In this case, the topography simply reflects the bedrock geology.

Question 10.2

(a) The strata at Shaftesbury dip southeast, because progressively younger strata crop out to the southeast (K4, K5, K6, G3...), while older strata occur to the northwest of the town.

(b) Assuming that the thickness of the strata does not change much, the dips are much steeper near Corfe Castle, because the outcrop widths are very narrow here, in contrast to the broad outcrops near Shaftesbury.

(c) The structure is a broad, strongly asymmetric, syncline, because younger rocks crop out in its core, and progressively older strata occur outwards on its limbs.

Question 10.3

(a) The sequence of rock units youngs to the north, therefore the strata are dipping roughly to the north.

(b) Between Llangynidr and SO (32) 2005, the sequence is reversed and older strata occur to the north, therefore the strata are dipping roughly to the south.

(c) The structure is a syncline, with the youngest rocks (C7) in the core.

(d) The strike direction is east–west, as shown by the roughly east–west stripes of the outcrops between Ammanford and Brynmawr.

(e) The strike direction is again east–west, as shown by the outcrop pattern between Margam and Caerphilly.

(f) The strike direction curves gently, but on average is roughly north–south, according to the outcrop pattern.

(g) Dip must be, on average, either to the east or to the west (i.e. at right angles to the strike direction). The map shows that younger strata occur to the west (from unit D1 in the east to unit C7 in the west), so the dip is to the west.

Question 10.4

Scarp slopes cutting through the resistant strata will face outwards from the core of the syncline, i.e. facing to the north on the northern limb of the syncline and to the south on the southern limb of the fold. See Figure 13.3.

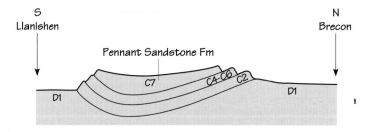

Figure 13.3   Answer to Question 10.4.

Question 10.5

The outcrop pattern on the northern limb of the syncline is, in general, wider than that of the same beds on the southern limb. Two possible reasons are:

- change in thickness of the beds. It is possible that all the beds are thinner in the south than in the north.
- change in dip. It is likely that the difference in outcrop width is due to a difference in the angle of dip between the northern and southern limbs. The northern limb will be at a shallower angle than the southern limb, as depicted in Figure 13.3.

Question 11.1

(a) The Cleveland Dyke (13 cm from southern end of the section on the North sheet).

(b) The Moine Thrust Zone (18–20 cm from the northwestern end of the section on the North sheet). This major fault zone is composed of several fault strands dipping gently east, which emplaced the Moine rocks over the Lewisian gneiss and Torridonian sandstones to the west.

(c) Beachy Head, <1 cm from the southeastern end of Section 1 on the South sheet. This is the only location along the section lines where Chalk crops out on the coast.

(d) The Lizard–Dodman–Start Thrust (1 cm from the southern end of Section 2). Most metamorphic rocks in the UK are much older than these, and the majority occur at the surface in the north and west of the UK.

(e) The Longmynd (24 cm from the northwestern end of Section 1), a block of older sediments uplifted by long-lived movement on fault systems close to the Welsh border.

You may wish to locate the features on the relevant sheet of the Bedrock UK Map, by measuring along the lines of section.

Question 11.2

(a) The general strike direction is east–west.

(b) Older beds occur going south from Lewisham in the sequence G3, G2, G1, K6, K5, K4, K3, K2. They must therefore dip to the north.

(c) Southwards from East Grinstead younger beds occur (from K2 to K6). They must be dipping to the south.

(d) The structure is an anticline. See Figure 13.4.

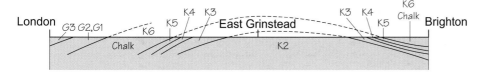

Figure 13.4   Answer to Question 11.2d.

(e) Yes, it is consistent. The Purbeck Group is the oldest Cretaceous unit exposed in the Weald, and this unit crops out near the centre of the anticlinal fold, where you would expect the oldest rocks to be exposed by erosion. (Note that all three small outcrops are bounded by faults on their northern edges. These faults may have played a part in the uplift of the rocks to the south, exposing these limited outcrops of Purbeck Group rocks.)

Question 11.3

(a) The four main areas are: southwest England; South Wales to the Mendips; North Wales and Anglesey; the Lake District.

(b) Outcrop patterns in all these four areas are much more complex than in most of the Bedrock UK Map (S).

(c) Igneous intrusions (showing up as large scarlet or crimson blobs) are common in three of the four areas: southwest England, North Wales/ Anglesey and the Lake District. Carboniferous–Permian (*CP*) granites dominate southwest England, with many smaller intrusions of the same age, or Devonian (*D*). In North Wales and Anglesey, the largest intrusions are Neoproterozoic (*X*), with several smaller Ordovician–Silurian (*OS*) bodies, especially on mainland Wales. The Lake District also boasts several Ordovician–Silurian (*OS*) intrusions, and a few Late Silurian– Devonian granites, e.g. near Shap (NY (35) 5509), and Skiddaw (NY (35) 3131). There are no large intrusions marked in the South Wales– Mendips region, though some small Ordovician–Silurian and Neoproterozoic bodies occur north of St Bride's Bay (in squares SM (12) 72 and SM (12) 82).

Question 11.4

(a) Mainly Triassic rocks (T2, T1) are found to the west of the fault.

(b) Mainly Carboniferous rocks (C8, C6 and C5), with a small outcrop of Ordovician (O1) near the north end of the fault trace, are found to the east of the fault.

(c) The beds in the west are the younger ones, so these would have been higher in the stratigraphic succession than those on the east side. Hence the west side must be the downthrown side.

Question 12.1

(a) This feature is (ii), a Palaeogene inlier. It is an outcrop of Thames Gp rocks (G3) surrounded by *younger* Neogene strata (Red Crag, Norwich Crag and Wroxham Crag; N2).

(b) The elongate blue outcrop is marked K4, which represents the Cretaceous Gault and Upper Greensand Formations, so it is not an igneous feature (neither a sill nor dyke). It is entirely surrounded by a narrow outcrop of older strata (Lower Greensand Group and Woburn Sand, K3), so this means it is an outlier. The correct description in this case is (i).

(c) This boundary is between the Cretaceous White Chalk Subgroup (K6) and the overlying Pliocene–Pleistocene strata (N2). There are no truncations shown in this segment of the boundary that betray its unconformable nature. The only evidence for an unconformity here comes from the stratigraphic column, which shows that there is a substantial time gap between the strata below (K6) and above (N2) the boundary. Several intervening units are missing from the stratigraphy here (potentially G1, G2, G3, G4, G5 and N1).

(d) Yes, because going north from the Humber, the base of the Cretaceous strata initially lies on Upper Jurassic (J6), then passes on to progressively lower beds down to the Lias (J1) at Market Weighton (SE (44) 8842), and then back on to Upper Jurassic (J6) inland of Filey (TA (54) 1280).

Acknowledgements

In addition to those mentioned in the Course Team list, the authors would like to thank Ian Parkinson for help with Chapters 2–4, and Helen Craggs for comments on the proofs.

Grateful acknowledgement is made to the following sources for permission to reproduce material in this book.

Figures

Cover: Andy Sutton.

Figure 1.2: NASA; Andy Tindle; Tom Argles; Nigel Harris; Figures 1.3a, 1.7, 1.12, 10.3a and b, 10.6, 10.15, 11.1b, c and e, 11.4, 11.6, 11.7 and 11.8: Reproduced with the permission of the British Geological Survey © NERC. All rights Reserved; Figures 1.3b 1.5, 2.4, 2.6, 2.7, 2.8, 2.9a, c and d, 2.10a and b, 2.13c, 2.14c, 2.16c, 2.18d, 3.4b, 3.5, 3.10, 3.11, 3.12, 4.3, 4.4, 4.5, 4.6, 4.9, 4.10, 4.12, 4.13, 4.16, 4.17, 4.18, 4.19, 4.20, 4.21, 4.22, 5.1, 6.1a, b and c, 6.3, 6.4, 6.5, 6.8, 6.10b and c, 6.11, 6.12, 6.13a, 6.14b, 7.1, 7.3, 7.4, 7.7, 7.10b, 7.12, 7.13a, 7.14, 8.1, 8.4, 8.6 and 8.7: Andy Tindle; Figure 1.6: John Watson, The Open University; Figure 1.8: Courtesy of the Geological Society; Figures 1.11b and c, 10.10, 10.12 and 10.15: Reproduced with the permission of Ordnance Survey on behalf of The Controller of Her Majesty's Stationery Office, © Crown Copyright. Licence Number Ed 100020607; Figure 1.13: Maureen Keogh/Flickr Photo Sharing; Figure 1.14: Reproduced with the permission of Ordnance Survey on behalf of The Controller of Her Majesty's Stationery Office, © Crown Copyright. Licence Number Ed 100020607; Reproduced with the permission of the British Geological Survey © NERC. All rights Reserved; United States Geological Survey; NASA; Figures 2.1, 2.9b, 6.10a and 7.10a: Peter Sheldon; Figure 2.10c: Joel Arem/Science Photo Library; Figure 2.17: Dr Naomi Williams; Figures 6.1d and 10.3c: Fiona McGibbon; Figure 6.1e: Scenesetters, Shropshire Geological Society; Figures 6.1f, 6.2 and 6.9a: David Rothery; Figure 6.7a: Bryan Storey; Figure 6.9b: Mark Davies; Figures 6.13b, 7.9a, 7.13b and 11.1d: Peter Webb; Figure 6.14a: National Museum & Galleries of Wales; Figures 7.2, 8.5, 10.2, 10.17b, 10.20b, 10.23a, 10.24a and 11.3: Tom Argles; Figure 7.9b: Cynthia Burek; Figures 7.11a and 9.1: Glynda Easterbrook; Figure 7.11b: J.A.Lees, Dept of Earth Sciences, University College London; Figure 10.3d: Duncan MacDonald; Figure 10.3e: Iain Gilmour; Figures 10.5 and 10.24a: CGIAR - Consortium for Spatial Information (CGIAR-CSI) http://srtm.csi.cgiar.org; Figures 10.1 (Moon) and 10.17a: USGS; Figure 10.9: Joe Dunckley/Flickr Photo Sharing; Figure 10.23b: USGS/University of Berkeley Collection; Figure10.24b: NASA; Figure 11.1a: Twiggles/Flickr Photo Sharing; Figures 11.1b, c and e, 11.4, 11.6, 11.7 and 11.8: Reproduced with the permission of the British Geological Survey © NERC. All rights Reserved; Figure 11.5: Angela Coe.

Index

Entries in **bold** represent glossary terms. Page numbers in *italics* refer to figures and tables.